MW00335410

CONTENT ADDRESSABLE PARALLEL PROCESSORS

COMPUTER SCIENCE SERIES

9,12, 15,17, 47, 63, 69, 91,

2/3

CONTENT ADDRESSABLE PARALLEL PROCESSORS

Caxton C. Foster

Computer and Information
Sciences Department

Graduate Research Center
University of Massachusetts
Amherst, Massachusetts

VNR Van Nostrand Reinhold Company
New York / Cincinnati / Atlanta / Dallas / San Francisco

Van Nostrand Reinhold Company Regional Offices:
New York Cincinnati Atlanta Dallas San Francisco

Van Nostrand Reinhold Company International Offices:
London Toronto Melbourne

Library of Congress Catalog Card Number: 75-31922
ISBN: 0-442-22433-8

Manufactured in the United States of America

Published by Van Nostrand Reinhold Company
450 West 33rd Street, New York, N.Y. 10001

Published simultaneously in Canada by Van Nostrand Reinhold Ltd.

15 14 13 12 11 10 9 8 7 6 5 4 3 2 1

Library of Congress Cataloging in Publication Data

Foster, Caxton C   1929–
   Content addressable parallel processors.

   (Computer science series)
   Bibliography: p.
   Includes index.
   1. Parallel processing (Electronic computers)
I. Title.
QA76.6.F67 1976   001.6′4   75-31922
ISBN 0-442-22433-8

For
Nedra
Alexander
Ann
Gregory
Prudence

Nothing in human life is more to be lamented, than that a wise man should have so little influence.

—Herodotus

PREFACE

Content Addressable Memories or Content Addressable Parallel Processors or Associative Memories or Associative Processors have been around the computing scene for almost 20 years now. Several hundred papers have been written discussing their use and design but so far no single text or reference book has tried to summarize the field. This volume attempts to remedy this lack. It attempts to gather into one place all the information that exists as of late 1975. The definition of what is a content addressable parallel processor and what is not is of necessity somewhat idiosyncratic. For example, the Holland Machine, Illiac IV and Staran are usually lumped together as "array processors." We consider only the last of these three. PEPE claims to have an associative processor at each element but this seems to be an overlap with our subject area in name only.

What *we* mean when *we* say "content addressable" is that at each memory cell of the machine there is sufficient logic to determine whether or not that particular cell holds data that match some criterion broadcast from the central control unit of the computer. That is, we *address* a cell on the basis of its *contents* rather than on the basis of *where* it is in memory. To use an old example we say "Will all cells containing the number 1234 please hold up your hands."

Once we have singled out a group of cells by a question such as the preceding one we wish to be able to do things to them. That is, we wish to *process* these cells in some fashion. Further, we wish to be able to perform this processing on all such cells simultaneously— that is in *parallel*. Hence the name of the book.

Chapter 1 is an introduction to the area and tries to give an overview of what a CAPP can do and why their widespread existence would benefit the computing fraternity. Chapter 2 continues the introduction with an example of a rather simple CAPP so the reader will have some idea of its structure and capability. Chapters 3 and 4 cover what is known of the theory of CAPPs and present three simple machines that allow one to apply this theory. Chapter 5 is a summary of the known algorithms for parallel processing. With most of these algorithms extensions to the hardware are suggested that will make these algorithms run quickly.

Chapter 6 is a collection of applications of CAPPs. These are intended to be suggestive rather than exhaustive. Chapter 7 reviews the extant papers on distributed hardware functions and Chapter 8 covers STARAN. Chapter 9 is a survey of some of the other CAPPs that have been built or described in the literature. Finally, Chapter 10 presents a summary of the rest of the book in the form of a suggested implementation of a CAPP.

This book grew out of notes for a course in Content Addressable Memories that has been presented several times at the University of Massachusetts. I particularly want to thank Elliot Soloway for reading the manuscript and in addition to pointing out many errors, making many positive suggestions that have improved the book no end. My thanks to all the students who took the course for their feedback; to Susan Kauffman for typing the manuscript; and to my wife and children for their patience with my mutterings and occasional (very occasional, of course) bad temper when the words wouldn't come.

Amherst, Massachusetts   CAXTON C. FOSTER

CONTENTS

CONTENT ADDRESSABLE PARALLEL PROCESSORS

1 | WHAT IS A CONTENT ADDRESSABLE PARALLEL PROCESSOR AND WHO NEEDS ONE?

There is an old New England story about the sailor who decided to retire from the sea. He said he was going to put an oar over his shoulder and walk inland until someone asked him what he was carrying. Last winter I was on the island of Antigua in the West Indies. A taxi driver asked me what I did and I replied that "I teach about computers." When he said "What are they?" I knew right away that was where I wanted to settle down. In the middle forties, the first electronic computers were being designed. Now, in the middle seventies, just thirty years later, almost every one has heard of computers, the majority of the American public has dealt with them in one fashion or another, and more people are engaged in building, programming, and operating computers than any other single type of mechanism except possibly automobiles.

John von Neumann is the man most responsible for making computers operate the way they do. His redesign of Eckert and Mauchly's Eniac set the tone for almost all present-day machines. A central processor, an input and an output organ, and a storage unit that has many individually addressable cells, each capable of holding one number to be used either as a datum or as an instruction is still the basic blueprint of a modern day computer. From an Intel 4004 micro-computer-on-a-chip through a Control Data Star, a Texas Instruments ASC or an IBM 370/195, all have the same fundamental framework. To be sure, one may be fast, another inexpensive, one may have sixteen central registers and another only one, but the storage in particular is almost interchangeable between machines except for details of width and speed. There exists a box called storage. The Central Processing Unit (CPU) presents this box with an address—the name of one particular cell—and after a brief delay, the box returns the contents of that one cell to the CPU. If a write is desired, the CPU gives the box the address and the number to write into that particular cell. No other operations are possible with Coordinate Addressed Storage.

Two other fundamental ways of organizing storage are known. These are called "pushdown stack" and "content addressable." Pushdown stacks are organized like a list. New items may be added to the top of the list or old items removed from the top. The order of entry is preserved and only the topmost element can be accessed. Machines like the B-5500, the KDF.9 and the PDP-11 have hardware designs which make a Coordinate Addressed Memory behave in some ways like a pushdown stack.

The remaining class, Content Addressable Memories (CAM's), are the subject of this book. As an illustration of what a CAM is and how it works, consider a professor trying to find out if some one of his students has a copy of a book called *Computer Architecture.* If he considers the students to be a Coordinate Addressed Memory, he asks: "Does the student in seat one have a copy of this book? Does the student in seat two . . .?" and so on, one at a time. In a pushdown stack model of the class, the professor stands by the door and as each student slips past him, asks the question.

If the professor assumes a Content Addressable Memory model, he stands before the class and says: "If you have a copy of this book, please hold up your hand." This of course presupposes a modicum of intelligence on the part of the students, a presumption which is probably contrary to fact. It also explains why a CAM is sometimes called a "distributed logic machine" or an "intelligent memory." There must be enough logic at each storage cell to enable it, at the very least, 1) to compare the number it holds with the number that is being broadcast from central control, and 2) to indicate match or mismatch by the state of a flip-flop (Rudolph, 1969).

For the purposes of this book, we will define a Content Addressable

Memory (CAM) to be a device capable of holding information, comparing that information with some broadcast information, and indicating agreement or disagreement between the two (Goodyear, 1965 B) and (Fuller, 1963).

We will define a Content Addressable Parallel Processor (CAPP) to be a CAM with the added ability to write in parallel into all those words indicating agreement. We may change the entire contents of the words, or only part, or even just one single bit of the agreeing words. This facility is called multi-write and it distinguishes CAM's from CAPP's. Given multi-write we can perform parallel arithmetic, compound searches, and in general emulate many of the features of array-type machines such as Illiac.

The first content addressable memory was proposed in 1956 (Slade, 1956). In 1972, Goodyear Aerospace Corporation placed Staran on the market as the first commercially available CAPP. In the intervening sixteen years, well over a hundred papers were published discussing the merits and applications of the concept (Minker, 1971 and Parhami, 1973).

Three basic reasons account for the long (for the computer industry) delay between conception and realization. The first of these is the expense. In 1973, one could buy Coordinate Addressed Storage ready-to-run with power supply, etc., for 2¢ a bit. Adding a second block of storage to Staran of 256 words by 256 bits (65Kbits) cost around $250,000 or $4 a bit. A cost differential of 200 to one. Using simplified logic and up-to-the-minute technology, one should be able to bring the cost ratio down to the order of two or three to one instead of two hundred.

But it is undeniable that CAPP's are more expensive than Coordinate Addressed Storage, and always will be because they require more circuitry than do conventional memories. It is the purpose of this book to show that speed of operation and ease of programming more than offset this differential.

The second reason why CAPP's have not become more widespread is that we are a very long way from having exhausted the potentials of conventional machines. Von Neumann's design is so powerful and so simple that everyone realizes that we have barely begun to explore the things that can be accomplished with the design already in hand. The few people pushing CAPP's are in the position of offering jam tomorrow to people drowning in honey today. The computer industry is manpower-bound, not architecture-bound. There are lots more problems waiting to be solved than there are people available to solve them. It is in this area, ironically enough, that CAPP's offer their greatest promise, as we shall see in the next section.

The third reason why CAPP's have not been an overnight success story is the same reason that seems to inhibit all new computer architectures. This is the conservatism—in its original sense—of computer programmers. Consider: The vice-president asks the installation manager about the new machine from *XYZ*. He goes to his programmers and asks them to evaluate the new design. They look at the design, find it difficult to understand because of its very differences and in a perhaps unconscious attempt to conserve their dearly won and highly valuable skills—the ability to program the machine already in the house—find all sorts of reasons why the old one is good and the new one is bad. Sometimes this is called insuring job security, sometimes it is called the NIH (not invented here) syndrome. Whatever it is called, it exists and is a stifling influence on the evolution of computers. Ask any Burroughs salesman how easy it is to sell a stack-oriented machine with a tagged architecture. Worse yet ask yourself how openly *you* responded to the last really novel idea in machine design you saw. The only way to surmount this problem is through education, to make the new familiar. That is another purpose of this book.

THE BENEFITS OF CAPP'S

There are two major advantages that can be obtained from Content Addressable Parallel Processors. These are speed of operation and ease of programming. The former is the simpler to explain and we will discuss it first.

Dr. Bernard Galler once defined repetition as being the multiplier that makes computers worthwhile. As any programmer knows, it is easier to work out a small problem by hand than to program, code, and debug it for machine execution. It is iterative loops, and perhaps recursion, that make computer solution worthwhile. Many, but by no means all, iterative loops apply a short string of code to independent chunks of data. Computation of a payroll is a classical example. Assuming the company can meet its bills, there is no interaction between the computation of the check for man *A* and for man *B*. The computer does one and then another and then another. There is no logical reason why these must be done sequentially. They are done that way because the computer can do only one thing at a time. CAPP's offer the opportunity to do many things at once. We can add or multiply thousands of pairs of items in no more time than it takes us to do one pair (Rudolph, 1971). To be sure, doing one pair in a CAPP in bit serial mode—which is what is forced on us by the structure of the CAPP—takes longer than doing it bit parallel on a conventional machine. But in a conventional machine if we have N identical computations to perform, it takes us N times as long as one such computation. Since in a CAPP we can do as many computations in parallel as we have room for, and since the room we have is limited only by our finances and not the inherent speed of semiconductor technology, the time required to execute N computations is independent of the number N.

There is a branch of computer science called Complexity Theory which is devoted to the study of how the execution time of various problems depends on the number of elements to be processed. For example, in a conventional machine, it takes time of order N to find the largest element of an array and it takes time of order N^2 to compare N elements each with all the others. In a CAPP, it takes time of order zero (independent of N) to do the first and time of order N to do the second. In Chapter 3 we study the theory of CAPP's and in Chapter 9 we examine several applications of CAPP's. It is fair to say that in most problems of interest, CAPP's reduce the execution time by one order of N. Problems that would have taken a time of order N^x take a time of order N^{x-1} when properly programmed on a CAPP. This is the first and best known appeal of content addressability, but it is subject to a rather peculiar challenge.

Given enough thought and ingenuity, it is often possible to find a scheme for a conventional computer that will reduce its execution time by one order of N. For example, CAPP's excel at doing catalog look up: Does element E exist in the catalog? It takes one probe of the memory to discover if the answer is yes or no. A straightforward linear search item by item takes an average of $N/2$ probes in a conventional machine. But if we generate a hash address from each item, and store the item at that address with links to an overflow table to take care of the cases when two items hash (map) onto the same address, it takes only $1\frac{1}{2}$ probes on the average to find an item. Conventional machine programmers point to such examples with justifiable pride and conclude that spending money for CAPP's is unnecessary given their own cleverness. Richard Hamming is reported to have remarked that: "The purpose of computers is insight, not numbers." One might turn this phrase somewhat to say that: "The purpose of computers is to give answers, not to give employment of programmers." This brings us to the second major advantage of CAPP's.

CAPP's are easier to program than conventional machines. As we proceed in our study of CAPP's, we will be wallowing in details of various algorithms. A casual observer might find the above statement that CAPP's are easy to program somewhat hard to swallow.

We spend considerable time in Chapter 8 discussing algorithms for CAPP's and some of them are formidable indeed. But how many programmers know how the sine routine in FORTRAN arrives at its answer or how floating point division hardware actually works? We spend this time in Chapter 8 because CAPP's are new and novel and their capabilities must be explored. In any commercial CAPP, most if not all of the algorithms of Chapter 8 would be wired (or microprogrammed) into the machine and the average user would know no more about them than he does about the hardwired algorithms of an IBM 360.

Once the basic algorithms are out of the way, CAPP's are easier to program than conventional machines. This is not to say that the instructions of a CAPP are easier to remember or write than those of a von Neumann machine, but rather that many problems of interest can be approached more naturally if content addressability is used.

In the first place, it takes time and cleverness to come up with a scheme like hash addressing and there is a surplus of neither in this world. As we mentioned above, there are more problems around to be solved than there are people around to work on them. If a CAPP offers a simple solution to a problem, it is only slightly less than insane to go around Robin Hood's barn in order to get to the same place another way. To say this another way, if all computers today had content addressability, no one in their right mind would dream of doing hash addressing. The former is not only easier to write, it is very much easier to debug.

Another point should be made. All programmers know that searching a table is bad. It wastes time. So in order to avoid such spawn of the devil they invent complicated algorithms to get around the need for searching. Examples are hard to pinpoint because many of the approaches to avoid searching have become part of our way of life, but consider the reputation of interpreters. They are bad! Why? Well, they are easy to write, easy to debug, and easy to modify, but they are *slow*. Why? Because they do a lot of searching. QED. It is impossible to estimate how much programmer and machine time have been spent avoiding searches, but it has to be a large amount of both.

CONCLUSION

At the present time, a conventional storage word of 32 bits might cost 50¢ while a word of content addressable storage might cost $2. But hardware prices have been dropping steadily and rapidly, whereas the cost of software has been rising equally rapidly. At present, the cost of an instruction to put into a 32 bit word is somewhere between $10 and $20. To be sure, some programs are replicated many times and the cost of writing them is amortized over the many copies while the cost of the hardware is incurred anew each time. But a very large class of programs are used in only one installation and hence cannot benefit from this cost sharing. Further, very few programs occupy storage permanently—resident operating systems being an obvious exception—and hence the cost of the storage they occupy must be shared over many programs. Thus, for many cases the difference in cost between conventional and content addressable storage is a vanishingly small fraction of the cost of problem solution. If content addressable computers were only 10% easier to program we could argue that a 100-instruction conventional program would cost (100 X 15) + (100 X 0.5) = $1550 while a content addressable program would cost [(100 − 10) X 15] + (100 − 10)2 = $1530, or almost an identical amount for instructions and storage together. The improvement in programmability is probably more likely 25% than 10%. If we add to this the increases in speed that can be obtained in many cases, it seems obvious that Content Addressable Parallel Processors will sweep all before them and become the standard of tomorrow. Perhaps if enough people read and believe the next 9 chapters, they will. (For somewhat less sanguine opinions, see Thurber, 1973 and Shore, 1973.)

2 | A MACHINE FOR DISCUSSION

In this chapter we are going to cover the design of a somewhat simplified but more or less typical Content Addressable Machine. We will use semiconductors as the design medium because it appears today (1975) that semiconductors will be the devices most likely to be used. We will compare the number of gates required for a CAM with the number required to make a conventional memory of comparable size. This will give the reader some idea of the cost of a CAM relative to ordinary memory. Then we will present a few basic algorithms for this machine and compare the execution times on a CAM with the times in a conventional machine. Having then the relative costs and performances of CAM's and RAM's (Random Access Memory), we will be able to compare one with the other intelligently.

THE STRUCTURE OF THE MEMORY

A Content Addressable Memory consists of a large number of cells, each several bits long. In our example we will choose 4096 cells by 32 bits or 128K bits total.

Figure 2.1 shows the overall design of a CAM. Information and commands are broadcast from the central control unit to every cell of memory. This takes place in parallel with every cell simultaneously

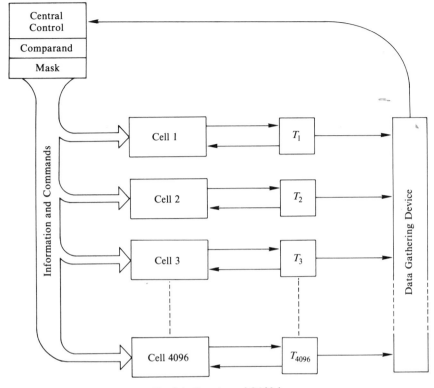

Fig. 2.1 Overview of CAM 1.

receiving the same signals. For example, the central control unit may tell the cells to compare the information they presently hold with the "comparand." Each cell has associated with it a tag bit T_i. The collection of tag bits will be referred to as the response store. There is a command (SET) which can be issued by the Central Control Unit which causes all the tag bits to be set to one. When the Central Control Unit issues a "compare" command, any cell containing a word which does *not* match the comparand will generate a signal that will cause its tag bit to be reset. After a "compare," then, only those cells whose contents equal the comparand will be left with their tag bits set.

Within the central control unit there are two registers called the Comparand Register and the Mask Register. When performing a simple search such as we are about to describe, the Comparand Register is used to hold the item we are looking for. But we may not want an exact match with the entire comparand. Perhaps we only want agreement on the first ten bits of the word. This is what the Mask Register is provided for. We put a word into the Mask Register which has ones where we wish to do a comparison and zeros everywhere else. If we wish to look only at the first ten bits of the 32-bit words we would use a mask such as:

$$1111 \quad 1111 \quad 1100 \quad 0000 \quad 0000 \quad 0000 \quad 0000 \quad 0000$$

Figure 2.2 shows the central command unit circuitry necessary to perform this function. If the jth bit of the mask is zero, neither match line $M1_j$ or MZ_j will be activated. If the mask contains a one in this bit position, then depending on whether the comparand has a zero or a one stored here, one of the match lines will be asserted and the other left inactive. These two match lines, $M1_j$ and MZ_j, go to the jth bit of every storage cell of the machine. They "broadcast" the contents of the comparand to each cell so that local comparison can take place.

Figure 2.3 shows the local circuitry at one of these storage cells (say the ith cell) required to perform a compare operation.

If either of the match lines ($M1$ or MZ) are energized in a particular

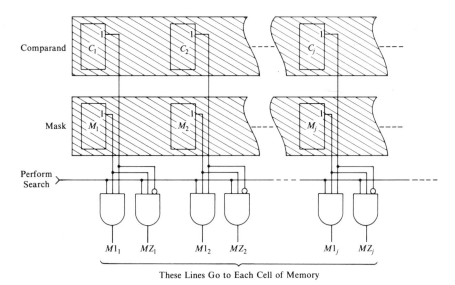

These Lines Go to Each Cell of Memory

Fig. 2.2 Details of the Comparand and Mask circuitry for performing the search operation.

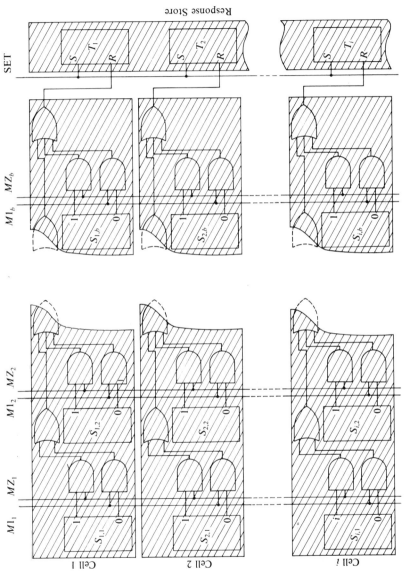

Fig. 2.3 The memory array of CAM 1.

bit position, then (letting S_{ij} stand for the jth bit of the ith cell) we have

$$M1_j \cdot \bar{S}_{ij} \vee MZ_j \cdot S_{ij}.$$

If the central control unit is looking for a *one*, and (S_{ij}) bit is *zero* or the CCU is looking for a *zero* and this bit is *one* then a mismatch signal will be generated at this bit and passed down the mismatch line to reset the tag bit (T_i) of this cell. If a word stored in this cell disagrees with the comparand at more than one bit position for which the mask contains *ones*, the effect is the same as if only one such instance occurred. If a word disagrees with the comparand only in a place or places where the Mask Register contains *zero* then no mismatch signal is generated and the tag bit of that word remains set (if indeed it was set to begin with). If a cell has its tag bit reset before a comparison takes place, there is nothing in the comparison process that will cause that tag bit to change. We can view the comparison operation as being a process of "winnowing;" discarding chaff and keeping only what is supposed to be the wheat.

The circuitry shown in Fig. 2.3 is not all that is required in a CAM. Four other functions must be implemented. They are Reading, Writing, Setting the response store, and Selecting the first responder.

READING

To read information out of a Content Addressable Memory, it is not necessary to provide any specific circuitry. As we shall see later in Chapter 4, a search and test procedure can substitute for read circuits. But for general convenience, we present a read circuit because it does not require a great number of gates and because it is much faster than the search algorithm.

To select a particular word for "reading" in a Coordinate Addressed Memory we present the memory box with the address of the cell whose contents are wanted and wait a few tenths of a microsecond until the desired information appears in the memory buffer register. But in a CAM there is no address associated with a cell. All we have to distinguish one cell from another is whether or not they are responders, i.e., have their tag bits set on. We will therefore make a virtue out of necessity and arrange to read out the contents of any cell that is a responder. (See Fig. 2.4.) If more than one word is a

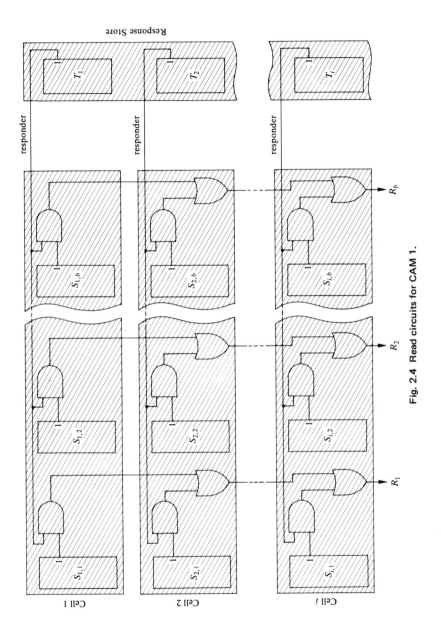

Fig. 2.4 Read circuits for CAM 1.

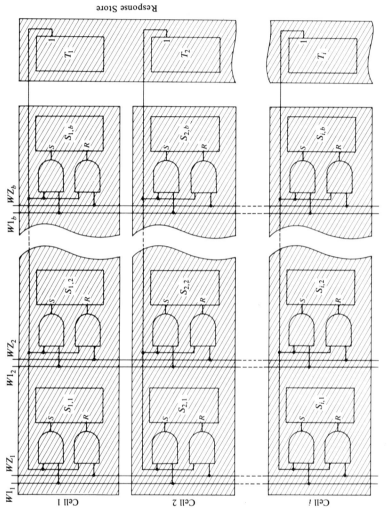

Fig. 2.5 Write circuits for CAM 1.

responder the read lines will contain the logical OR (an "inclusive or" circuit; giving an output of ONE if any of its inputs are ONE) of the contents of all the responders.

WRITING

In this introductory CAM we are going to provide a facility some-times called Multiwrite. This is the ability to write, in parallel, into as many words as are responders, all at the same time. Just as we used the responder/nonresponder distinction to select the cell (or cells) to be read from, we will use the same criterion to decide which words are to be written into. Figure 2.5 shows the write circuits at each bit of memory. If we wish to write a one into the jth bit of all responders we energize the $W1_j$ line. Where the responder line is also energized, a one will be stored. Where the responder line is not energized, no change in the information stored will take place.

If we don't wish to write into some particular bit of the responders we simply don't energize either $W1$ or the WZ line of that bit. We can, therefore, given appropriate central control circuits, write into any bits of the cells that are responders which we choose. We may write into only one field or we may write into the whole cell.

COMPARISON WITH A RAM

Figure 2.6 summarizes the design of the CAM bit so far. Allowing two gates to construct the flip-flop we need nine gates per bit of content addressable storage. If we allow for tri-state logic and wired

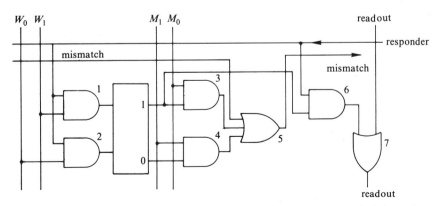

Fig. 2.6 One bit of a CAM using 9 gates including those required to store the information.

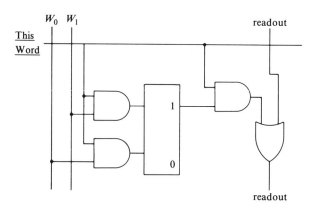

Fig. 2.7 One bit of a coordinate addressed memory using six gates, including those needed to store information.

OR's, then gates 5 and 7 could be eliminated and the gate count reduced to seven. Figure 2.7 shows one bit of a Random Access Memory for comparison. We still need two gates to control writing, two to store the information and two (one of them of wired-OR type) to control readout. Selection of the "this word" line is done by some external selection (addressing) circuitry. This gives a ratio of 9/6 (or 7/5 if we allow wired ORs) between the number of gates required to make a bit of CAM and a bit of RAM. Since semiconductor prices seem to go by the amount of area required, we can estimate that CAM's will always cost between 1.4 and 1.5 times as much as RAM's. When the price eventually drops to $1 for 1000 32-bit cells of RAM, paying $1.50 for the same amount of CAM won't seem exorbitant. But, then again, perhaps it will because if I budget X dollars for purchasing memory I can get $\frac{1}{3}$ more of RAM than I can of CAM.

Only if the performance and/or the ease of programming of a CAM is, say, twice as good as for a RAM will people spend those extra pennies. We will look at a couple of examples of high performance CAM algorithms in the next section but first we must present the remaining two functions provided in our CAM.

SET

So far we have discussed only those constituents of a CAM that will allow us to turn off a tag bit. These were the mismatch circuits. If we want to be able to turn these tag bits back on again, we must provide some circuitry to accomplish this. Figure 2.8 shows a line

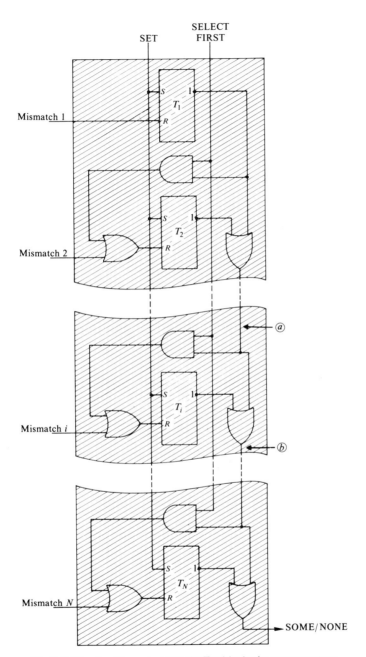

Fig. 2.8 The circuits surrounding the Tag bits in the response store.

called the Set line which runs to the set input of each and every tag bit. When energized by central control, it will turn *on* all the tag bits.

SELECT FIRST RESPONDER

There will be times when more than one cell of the memory is responding to some search. Further, there will be occasions when we wish to single out just one of these responders and deal with it alone. To provide this capability, we organize the cells of the memory to the extent that each cell has a predecessor and a successor. That is, we "string" them on a wire like beads in a necklace. In this sense then, there is always an "earliest" or "first" responder, the one nearest the beginning of the string. Using the circuits of Fig. 2.8 we provide the function "select first responder." This turns off the tag bit of any cell whose predecessor, or the predecessor of whose predecessor, or indeed any of whose "ancestors" is on. Suppose first that the ith cell is the first responder. Then the SOME/NONE line at the point labelled a will have no signal on it because no earlier cell has a tag bit turned on. But at point b and at all following cells the SOME/NONE line will be energized by the fact that $T_i = 1$. Then when the select first line is energized, each of these succeeding tag bits will be reset just as if they had held a mismatch. The SOME/NONE line is also used to tell the central control unit that some, or none, of the cells have their tag bits set: that is, to tell the central control whether or not there are any "responders" to the previous search.

Once the first responder has been selected and processed, it can be marked in some fashion (by writing in one of its bits) to indicate that it is finished. Subsequent searches can then be adapted to discover only unprocessed cells. This way all the responders to a search may be taken in turn, one at a time.

FIND THE GREATEST

In order to bring out some of the capabilities of a CAM, so that they can be kept in mind while going through the more theoretical chapters immediately following this one, we will present two algorithms at this point. Many other algorithms will be found in Chapter 8. The first of these algorithms will be to find the largest word stored in the

CAM. We will assume here that all the words are positive, and that they are all different.

The flow diagram for one algorithm for finding the largest number is shown in Fig. 2.9. The initial contents of the mask and comparand registers is shown at the top of the diagram. The mask has one in the left-most (most significant) bit and the rest are zeros. The comparand is all ones to start out with. By the time we finish the mask will be all ones and the comparand will hold a copy of the largest word in the array.

We begin by setting all the tag bits and then looking for an exact match to the masked comparand. The first time through this selects all those cells holding a one in their most significant bit position.

Now we test to see if there are any responders, that is, if there are any cells with a leading one. If not, we know that the largest word must have a zero in this position. So we change the bit of the comparand we were just examining to zero. We are not finished so we put an additional one into the mask and go back to search again

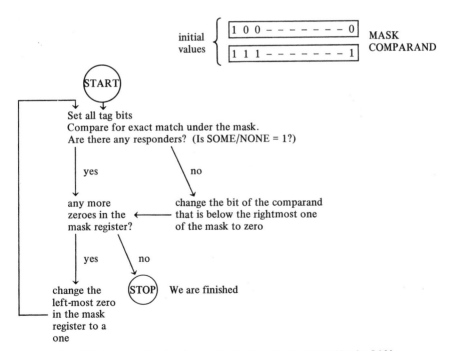

Fig. 2.9 An algorithm for discovering the largest word stored in the CAM.

for an exact match, this time to the first two bits of the comparand. The second bit of the comparand is one and the first bit agrees with the first bit of the largest word. Suppose for a moment we found some responders the previous pass, so that we left C_0 equal to 1. There are four possible ways that words can have two high order bits:

1) 00 $X X X$ . . .
2) 01 $X X X$ . . .
3) 10 $X X X$
4) 11 $X X X$

We already know that there are some words stored of either class 3 or class 4, so we wish to ignore all words of classes 1 and 2. This we will do because the leftmost bit of the comparand is 1. Now we ask if any words of class 4 are stored. If not, the largest stored word must belong to class 3. If there are any then the largest word will be found among that class.

We proceed round and round the loop, each time dividing the remaining class of words in half, $101XX$ . . . and $100XX$, discovering if any of the larger types exist and narrowing our attention to the largest class known to exist.

As we proceed across the word from left to right, the comparand grows to look more and more like the largest word in the array and by the time we have gotten to the right hand end we have extracted a copy of the desired word and built it up bit-by-bit in the Comparand Register. The reader should note particularly that this algorithm is "bit serial" and "word parallel;" that is, we process all words simultaneously but one bit at a time.

ADD ONE

The second algorithm we will explore here is that required to add the number one to every word in memory in parallel. This algorithm is also word parallel and bit serial. This will serve as an example of parallel processing and give a hint of the arithmetic ability of a CAM. Once again, more sophisticated algorithms will be postponed to Chapter 8.

We begin by reserving the left-most bit of each cell to serve as a carry bit. Again, we assume only positive integers for convenience. The algorithm (see Fig. 2.10) starts by setting an index variable j

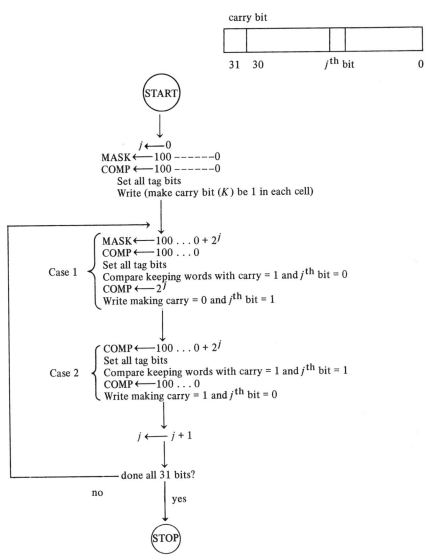

Fig. 2.10 An algorithm for adding 1 to every word in the memory.

(stored in the central control unit) to be equal to 0, the right-most bit position. We then set all tag bits and write K—the carry bit—as a 1 in every cell of memory. This represents the quantity that must be added to each cell.

There are two situations that must be taken care of. When the carry bit is 1 and the jth bit of a cell is 0 and when the carry bit is 1 and the jth bit of a cell is also 1. (When the carry bit is 0, those cells are all finished and drop out of the operation.) In the first case we wish to write $K = 0$, $B_j = 1$, while in the second we should write $K = 1$, $B_j = 0$. The algorithm shown does exactly this and then increments j by one and repeats until all 30 bits have been processed.

Question 2.1: Reversing the order of treating the two cases $K = 0$, $B_j = 1$ and $K = 1$, $B_j = 0$ will lead to trouble. Why?

Question 2.2: It should be possible much of the time to decrease the number of iterations of this algorithm by adding another test. What test?

COMPARISON WITH ALGORITHMS FOR RAM's

One supposes that the algorithms employing conventional storage for finding the largest item and for adding one to each word are obvious to readers of this book. Suppose there are N items, each of B bits in length. Then the algorithms for RAM's take times which are proportional to N while those for CAM's take times proportional to B. In the one case, operations are bit parallel, and word serial, while in the other they are word parallel and bit serial. Both algorithms presented above could be realized in hardware with consequent higher speed for either CAM or RAM machines.

Probably the most important message of this chapter is that CAM's can do some very interesting things and they can do them in a fixed time even if the number of items to be processed grows very large.

Not all CAM operations are bit serial, although we will find in Chapter 8 that many of them are. The reader might find it interesting to try to design a memory that could "add one to all words" in a time not dependent on B, ignoring carry propagation times, of course.

3 | SOME THEORETICAL RESULTS

In this chapter, we are going to discuss the background to one of the few theoretical studies of CAM's that are known (Foster, 1965). We will look at the problem of taking an iterative loop and executing the whole thing in a parallel fashion. The mode of attack is to find ways of expressing all executable statements of FORTRAN in a single canonical form. Certain descriptors of this form are then considered and a few typical algorithms are categorized.

ALGORITHMS VERSUS PROBLEMS

We are going to concentrate on the parallel execution of algorithms, rather than on the parallel solution of problems. The reason for this is clear. Knowing the problem does not permit one to say "such and such is the set of all algorithms that solve this problem." In fact, to do so would contradict M. Gödel and Church. That means that we can never know if we have found the *best* algorithm for parallel execution. Perhaps it lies just around the next corner.

If we look only at algorithms, however, this problem disappears. We have a definite procedure in front of us which has definite characteristics. Our task is then only to describe these characteristics. Once that is done, careful reading of this and the succeeding chapter will enable one to say how much hardware will be required to execute that algorithm in parallel, but not how much hardware is needed to solve the problem.

Consider the following example: Given feedback to central control of the exact number of responders to a search, one can easily write an algorithm that will add up the elements of a vector in parallel (see Chapter 8). That is, we form:

$$X = \sum_{i=1}^{n} Y_i.$$

But given the same hardware it is not possible to execute the algorithm:

$$X = 1$$
$$\text{DO } 10 \qquad I = 1,N$$
$$10 \qquad X = X * Y(I)$$

which forms

$$X = \prod_{i=1}^{N} Y_i$$

in parallel.

If, however, we choose to store the elements Y_i as their logs rather than as their magnitudes, it is very easy to form the product (by summing the logs) but not to form the sum. We therefore confine our attention to algorithms.

CONSTRUCTING PROGRAMS

In 1968, Bohm and Jacopini (Bohm, 1968) showed that all flow diagrams, and hence all programs, could be expressed using a very limited set of primitives. Combining their results with earlier, but not especially lucid work by the present author (Foster, 1965), we are going to show that all programs can be constructed using their pushdown stack (for control purposes) and a single primitive operation called the "Iterated Simple Conditional." We can then concentrate our attention on the Iterated Simple Conditional (ISC) and see what characteristics it has.

Bohm and Jacopini describe three primitive functions. These are "sequence," "repetition," and "selection." They are shown in symbolic form in Fig. 3.1. Squares represent operations or sub-programs,

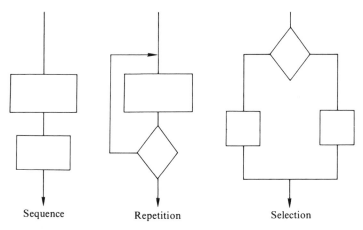

Sequence   Repetition   Selection

Fig. 3.1 Fundamental operations for flow diagrams.

while diamonds represent choices between two control paths. Sequence is simply the execution of one block after another. Repetition involves continued execution of a block as long as some condition holds, and selection involves executing either one block or another, depending on the value of some variable.

In addition to these functions, they employ a special pushdown stack on which four operations may be performed:

T–put a 1 on the top of the stack
F–put a 0 on the top of the stack
K–pop up the stack discarding the top element
W–branch on the value in the top of the stack

We will not go through the arguments presented by Bohm and Jacopini but will accept their conclusions that all flow diagrams can be expressed using these elements. Now we propose a single, rather complicated control structure that is equivalent to repetition and selection. This control structure is called an "Iterated Conditional," or IC for short. It has the following format:

FOR ⟨index⟩ = 1 UNTIL ⟨$B1$⟩ IF ⟨$B2$⟩ THEN ⟨S⟩

which may be read as:

Set the index variable to 1. If condition $B2$ is true, execute statement S. If $B2$ is false, do not execute S. Then increment the index variable by 1 and if $B1$ is false, repeat the test of $B2$ and execution (or nonexecution) of S. When $B1$ becomes true, exit to the next statement. The statement S may be another nested ISC or it may be an assignment statement of the form:

$$\langle\text{variable}\rangle \longleftarrow \langle\text{expression}\rangle. \quad \text{(See Fig. 3.2.)}$$

It is not difficult to see that this provides the same control structures as repetition and selection. By ignoring the index variable, if we so desire, the loop on UNITL$\langle B1\rangle$ forms a "do until" structure which, by inverting the sense of $B1$, is equivalent to a "do while" or repetition structure.

If $B1$ of an IC is always true (for example 1 = 1) we can simplify an IC and write it as a one-way-if. Selection can then be represented as:

$$\text{If} \quad B2 \text{ then } S1$$
$$\text{If} \neg B2 \text{ then } S2$$

and depending on the value of $B2$, we "select" either Statement 1 or statement 2 for execution.

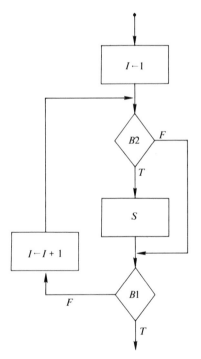

Fig. 3.2 The structure of an Iterated Conditional (IC).

In what follows we are going to concentrate on those IC's for which $B1$ is a condition on the index variable. That is, we wish to consider cases which could be expressed by FORTRAN DO loops. The condition $B1$ we choose is "⟨index⟩$>N$" where N is a constant. We will call these "Iterated Simple Conditionals" or ISC's. We make no claim here that all control structures can be cast as collections of ISC's. It is merely that we will find these more amenable to further discussion.

Disinterleaving

While we may include from the above that all control structures may be expressed as a sequence of IC's, there exist cases in which it is desirable to simplify the control structures so generated. Consider a case such as this one expressed in FORTRAN:

```
        DO 10 I = 1,100
          S1
          S2
     10 CONTINUE
```

where $S1$ and $S2$ are two statements. We would like to "disinterleave" the two statements and generate a program of the form:

```
        DO 10 I = 1, 100
          S1'
     10 CONTINUE
        DO 20 I = 1, 100
          S2'
     20 CONTINUE
```

where $S1'$ and $S2'$ are like $S1$ and $S2$, except possibly for housekeeping details, and the state of the data after exiting from the second loop is the same as it would have been in the previous case where $S1$ and $S2$ were contained in a single loop. Sometimes the two loops fall apart naturally with no problems at all; sometimes they require a certain amount of cleverness to disentangle. A rigorous, impractical, but amusing formal procedure exists which guarantees that they are separable. It involves the use of Gödel numbers. The Gödel number of a string of n numbers $a, b, c, \ldots, z$ can be found by raising the first n primes not including 1 to the power equal to that element of the original string and multiplying the results together. Thus:

$$G(a, b, c, \ldots, z) = 2^a \times 3^b \times 5^c \times \ldots \times P_n^z$$

The method of separation is as follows: Assume a loop which on the ith pass executes statements e and f and assume that they leave resultants E_i and F_i. Then define h_0 which computes the Gödel number of the original contents of E_i and F_i (for each i, of course) and leaves the resulting number in E_i.

Next define h_1, which is like "e followed by f," except that where it requires any of the initial values of E_i or F_i it takes them from the Gödel number stored in E_i. Further, h_1 stores a single resultant (the Gödel number of the results of e) in E_i. Note that h_1 having a single resultant is simple. Next, define h_2 which decodes the Gödel number in E_i for the value to put into F_i; and finally, define h_3 to decode E_i for the real value to put into E_i.

Then, executing h_0, h_1, h_2, and h_3 in turn achieves the same results as executing the compound conditional involving e and f.

I doubt very much if anyone will ever actually do the above. Nonetheless, it is a proof, for whatever that is worth.

Alignment

Suppose we have an assignment statement of the type:

$$A(I) = B(I + 5) + C(I + 6).$$

For each value of the index variable, this statement references three separate cells of memory, namely the Ith, the $I + 5^{th}$, and the $I + 6^{th}$. But if we have a wide enough memory cell, we can store three fields within each cell. For example, we might store $A(I)$, $B(I)$, and $C(I)$ in the Ith cell of the data vector. This is traditionally called "packing." If the above statement is the only one which references this particular data vector, or more accurately, the only one which simultaneously needs to use A, B, and C, then we can realign the three vectors A, B, and C so that $A(1)$, $B(b)$, and $C(7)$ fall into the same cell. If it proves practical in a particular case to do this, then we will assume that it has been done.

FOUR DESCRIPTORS

Now that we have defined ISC's and discussed disinterleaving and realignment, we are ready to look at the four different descriptors of

ISC's. These are: mode of address, number of internal operands, depth of nest, and interpass coupling. The reason we want to examine these descriptors will become clear when we get to Chapter 4. There we will see that for different values of the descriptors, different kinds of hardware are required to execute the ISC's in a time independent of the number of cells to be processed.

In what follows, we will need a definition of a "resultant." It is the variable on the left-hand side of an assignment statement, namely, the one that gets changed by having the result of the computation of the expression stored into it. Symbolically, an assignment statement is:

$$\langle resultant \rangle \longleftarrow \langle expression \rangle$$

Modes of Address

There are five modes of address that have been used in digital computers: (1) direct, (2) indirect, (3) immediate, (4) relative, and (5) tag.

In the direct mode, the instruction word contains the address (coordinate) of a cell that contains the operand. In the indirect mode, the instruction word contains the address of a cell, which in turn contains the address of a second cell in which is the operand. In the immediate mode, the contents of the address field of the instruction word itself are used as the operand. In the relative mode, a cell containing the operand is specified, not by giving its absolute address (coordinate), but by giving its location relative to the address at which this instruction is stored. An absolute address then is assigned either at load time or at execution time, depending on the type of computer being used. In the tag mode of addressing, the contents of a certain field are specified, and a search is instituted for a cell that bears this tag (has these specified contents). The remaining contents of this cell are then used as the operand.

Any of these modes can be indexed. This causes the contents of a specified index register to be added to the address field of the instruction before interpretation is begun. The span of a loop is defined as the set of memory locations that in a conventional computer begin with L_0 and end with $L_0 + N$, where N is the upper limit of the iteration. Consider an iterative loop that applies some operation Q successively to all the operands within its span. If on the ith pass through the loop, each cell that contains the required operands can be located by a linear transformation on i, the mode of address is called direct.

As an example, a sequence of operations, each perhaps with a different base address but all referring to the same index register, is said to be directly addressed. Thus, the contents of Cell $(100 + i)$ can be added to the contents of Cell $(200 + i)$ for all values of i from 0 through 50. This is considered to be a directly addressed operation.

Immediate addressing can be viewed as a form of direct addressing in which the coordinate address of the operand is that of the instruction register.

If, however, the directly addressed cells contain not the operands themselves, but information about where or how the actual operands can be found, the mode is not direct. If the contents of the directly addressed cells give the coordinate addresses of the cells containing the operands, the mode is called indirect. This definition can be extended recursively to many levels.

Tag addressing is similar to indirect addressing in that a name or identifying tag describing the cell that contains the operand is to be found in the directly addressed cell. For indirect addressing, the memory is assumed to be ordered according to these tags (the coordinates), and thus no scanning of the memory is required to find the desired cell. For the tag mode, on the other hand, the memory is assumed to be unordered. In addition, instead of the identifying tag (name) being stored implicitly in the address decoding tree, it must be stored explicitly in the cell itself. Because of the lack of order, a conventional memory must be scanned to find the cell bearing the desired tag in tag mode addressing.

Finally, the relative addressing mode in the past has been applied mostly within an instruction sequence, but the concept can be generalized. If the memory is assumed to be imbedded in some space, each cell will have neighbors. By relative addressing, both a direction and a distance in this space between the directly addressed cell and a neighbor, the desired cell, can be specified (for example, three squares East and two North).

Thus, there are three basic types of addressing modes to be considered:

1. Direct (including immediate). The cell addressed contains the operand.
2. Relative. The cell addressed contains the positional displacement at which the operand can be found.
3. Tag (including indirect). The cell addressed contains the "name" of the cell holding the operand.

Number of Internal Operands

Every iterated simple conditional has two sets of operands: the internal (V) and the external (E), either of which, but not both, may be null. An operand common to all passes through the iteration is called an external operand. An operand whose selection depends on the value of the index of iteration is called internal. Thus, in a FORTRAN DO loop, any subscripted variable (for which the subscript is a function of the indexing variable of the loop) is an internal operand. Any nonsubscripted variable is external, and any subscripted variable whose subscript does not contain the index variable of this particular loop is external to this loop, although it may be internal to another loop. Thus, in the following program segment:

$$DO \quad 10 \quad I = 1,N$$
$$10 \quad IF \quad X(I) \ .LE.3, \ Y(I) = ABLE + Z(J) * BAKER(I + J)$$

X, Y, and BAKER are internal operands while the numbers 3, ABLE, and Z are external to this loop.

Note that to each and every X_i there corresponds a unique Y_i. Therefore, it would be possible to store X_i in one field of Cell i and Y_i in another field of the same cell; to align them. We assume that all desirable alignment has been done, so for some reason these variables are treated as being distinct and we will honor that unknown reason here. On this basis, the number of internal operands in the preceding program is three.

For tag addressing, we assume that each memory cell has a tag field T and one or more data fields: X, Y, Z, etc. Then $Y\{K\}$ will be taken to mean "the contents of the Y field of that cell in memory whose tag field T holds a pattern identical to the pattern stored in variable K."

Suppose a list of tags are stored in a vector T. Assume now that on each iteration of a loop we wish to tag address a different cell by indexing through T. Then on each pass there are two internal operands to be retrieved: first the tag and then the cell it points to. Thus, each occurrence of tag or relative addressing inside a loop will add one to the number of internal operands.

If the number of internal operands is equal to one, the iterated conditional is called "monadic." If the number is greater than one, it is called "polyadic." (Note that tag or relative addressing must be polyadic.)

If several iterated simple conditionals are nested within one outer loop, the general principle to be observed is as follows:

"If Cell i and Cell j are both internal operands
and if in operating on Cell i, distinct from j,
the contents of Cell j are referenced, the loop
containing this operation is polyadic, and any
outer loops containing this one are also polyadic."

Depth of Nest

If two iterated conditionals are nested, one within the other, the inner one is said to have depth one, provided it does not itself contain another iteration, and the outer is said to have depth two. An operation that is performed only once (for example, initializing an external operand to zero) is said to have depth zero. In general, the count increases from the inside out, with each succeeding enveloping iteration having a depth larger by one than the greatest depth that it contains. This direction of counting was chosen, rather than its more conventional opposite, so that a subsegment of an algorithm could be discussed without considering the external context. Thus, a particular sequence of operations has the same depth whether it stands alone or is imbedded in some larger program.

Interpass Coupling

The discussion on the number of internal operands, above, is concerned with the interaction *between cells on a single pass.* Here, the effects of *the execution or nonexecution of Pass* i *on Pass* j, distinct from i, are analyzed.

Consider first an ISC with exactly one resultant from its single substitution statement on each pass. Let the resultant of the ith pass be called $r(i)$, the set of internal operands of the ith pass be called $V(i)$, and the set of external operands that serve in this case as inputs to the operation be called E.

Four types of interaction between passes ("coupling") can be distinguished.
Uncoupled:

$$r(i) \notin E \cup V(j) \quad \text{for } (j \neq i).$$

The resultant of the ith pass is not written into any external operand whose contents serve as input to the operation, nor into any location used to store an internal operand for any pass j distinct from i. This leaves only two places in which the resultant can be stored: (1) into an external operand whose initial (at the beginning of this pass) contents are not examined, or (2) into a member of $V(i)$ that is unique to the ith pass.

As an example,

FOR $I = 1,N$	IF $A(I)$.EQ.1	THEN FLAG $= 1$

puts a ONE in the flag register every time a cell is found in $A(1)$ through $A(N)$ containing a ONE. If the value of flag is set to ZERO before entering the loop, this will serve as an OR operation over the whole span of the iteration.

As a second example,

FOR $I = 1,N$	IF $A(I)$.EQ.1	THEN $B(I) = B(I) + 2$

adds two to the contents of the b-field of every cell that has an a-field containing a ONE. Thus, the resultant $r(i)$ is stored in the b-field of Cell i, and since each value of the index is assumed only once, this cell is never re-examined.

Finally,

FOR $I = 1,N$	IF $A(I)$.EQ.1	THEN $B(I + 3) = 0$

puts a ZERO in the b-field of Cell $i + 3$ whenever the a-field of i is ONE. But the b-field of the cells does not serve as an input to the operation. As far as this program segment is concerned, the b-fields of the cells initially could contain all ZEROs, or all ONEs, or a mixture of the two. There would be no change in the behavior of this segment.

Externally coupled:

$$r(i) \notin V(j) \quad \text{for } (i \neq j) \text{ but } r(i) \in E.$$

The resultant of the ith pass is used to modify the contents of an external operand whose initial contents were examined in order to determine the resultant. Two types of externally coupled operations can be distinguished: symmetric and asymmetric. Before distinguishing between these types, two definitions must be made. An operation is said to be "executable" in a *character serial mode* if it can be applied first to the least significant characters of every operand, generating a resultant and perhaps a carry, then applied to the next least significant character, then to the third, and so forth. An operation is said to be *bubblable* if for any given character position, the relative location of the various values of this character in the array is not relevant to the result and if only the number of occurrences of each value is considered. An operation is bubblable if all the ones in a particular column could be "bubbled" up to one end of the memory. Another way of saying this is to say that the result of the operation would be the same if the relative order of execution of the various passes was changed. Thus, for example, the operation which counts the number of cells that are responders to a search is bubblable. If there are three responders there are still three responders whether they are in cells 1, 2, and 3 or cells 72, 169, and 3280.

Those operations that are bubblable and can be executed in a character serial mode are called "symmetrically externally coupled." Which operations are symmetric depend in part on the method of representing numbers in the memory. If TWO's complement binary is used, addition is symmetric and multiplication is not. But if the logarithm of the number, rather than the magnitude is stored in binary form, the reverse is true.

Those operations that are not symmetric are called asymmetric. For example,

| FOR $I = 1,N$ | IF 1.EQ.1 | THEN $S = S + A(I)$ |

which sums up all the *a*-fields, is symmetrically externally coupled, whereas

| FOR $I = 1,N$ | IF 1.EQ.1 | THEN $P = P * A(I)$ |

which multiplies them, is asymmetrically externally coupled.

An iterated simple conditional of depth two or more is called "coupled between levels" if an inner loop is externally coupled to a variable that is an internal operand of the outer loop. It can be either symmetrically or asymmetrically coupled.

Note that this property of symmetry is stronger than simple commutativity. To be commutative, it is sufficient that the interchange of two operands does not affect the results. But to be symmetric any particular byte of one operand must be interchangeable with the corresponding byte of the other operand, leaving the rest of the bytes as they were, and still have no effect on the result. For example, multiplication is commutative: $376 \times 582 = 582 \times 376$; but it is not symmetric: $376 \times 582 \neq 576 \times 382$.

Internally coupled:

$$r(i) \in V(j) \quad \text{for } (i \neq j).$$

The resultant of the ith pass is written into a location used as one of the internal operands for Pass j. Here it makes a great deal of difference whether Pass j is executed before or after Pass i. As an example of an internally coupled operation, consider:

| FOR $I = 1,N$ | IF 1.EQ.1 | THEN $A(I) = A(I) + A(I-1)$ |

which adds to the a-field of each cell the accumulated sum of the initial a-fields, of all previously contacted cells.

Operations, such as this one, in which the order of execution is important, cannot be executed in parallel. Priority is important, and simultaneous execution would lead to undefined results. In essence, one would be trying to both read from and write into a cell at the same time.

DISCUSSION OF DESCRIPTORS

As mentioned at the beginning of this chapter, it is not possible to characterize problems in and of themselves. As an example, there are at least two ways of selecting the greatest number in an array. In a sequential computer, the natural method would be to compare the first number of the array with each succeeding number until one is found that exceeds it. The first number would be replaced with this new larger number and the operation would continue, always keeping the largest number yet found as the comparand. In one pass this procedure would select the greatest element from the array. It would be a monadic, directly addressed, depth one, externally coupled (through the changing comparand), asymmetric algorithm.

Next, consider the algorithm presented in Chapter 2. This algorithm is parallel-by-word, serial-by-bit, monadic, directly addressed, depth two, with an uncoupled inner loop.

Thus, it can be seen that two algorithms for solving the same problem differ in the values of their descriptors, one being uncoupled and the other externally coupled. It is clear that these descriptors do not apply to problems but rather to methods proposed for their solution. If one is fortunate, he might discover a method for a given problem that fits into a particular characterization. But if one fails to find such a method, it does not necessarily imply that none exists. Of what use, then, are these descriptors? Exactly this: given a proposed method of solving a problem (an algorithm), it is possible to determine if a proposed hardware configuration can permit parallel execution of this algorithm. Should the answer be yes, well and good. Should it be no, either a different method or a different machine must be proposed. But the descriptors, as such, offer no guide as to how to go about this task.

Another drawback to this characterization of algorithm is that the descriptors are not entirely independent. For example, if an algorithm is monadic it must be directly addressed because either relative or tag addressing refers to a second cell for the actual data. Again, if the algorithm is of depth one, it cannot involve tag addressing because in that mode, each cell must scan the array for its own data, involving a minimum of two levels of nest.

Nonetheless, there are several reasons why this set of descriptors was chosen.

1. They are natural; that is, they correspond in major part to concepts already in use within the field of computation or the theory of automata.
2. They are readily recognizable. Once the concepts have been delineated, specific algorithms in the standard format are easy to classify without ambiguity.
3. They permit proofs. Using these descriptors, it is possible to develop proofs about the abilities of various machines.
4. They conform to the functions that have been distributed. There is a correspondence between the values assigned to the descriptors and the kinds of functions that must be distributed for parallel execution. Thus, polyadic algorithms require intercell communication; symmetric externally coupled algorithms require quantitative feedback; and the tag addressing mode requires some form of redefinable neighborhood.

These reasons might be applied equally well to some other set of descriptors than the ones chosen for study, and perhaps with greater cogency.

A CLASSIFYING ALGORITHM

To make this set of descriptors more useful, an algorithm is presented here that can be applied to any computer program and that will generate the values the descriptors assume for that program. This algorithm has the following steps:

1. Express the program in the FORTRAN language using only DO loops and simple conditionals.
2. Using either the intuitive methods or the formal procedure involving Gödel numbers express the innermost loops of the program as strings of iterated simple conditionals.
3. Whenever within a DO loop there exist two vector variables A and B such that A and B occur at least once with identical subscripts, let the two variables be stored in two fields of one set of memory cells.
4. Beginning with the innermost loops and working outward, execute the following steps:
   a. If there are DO loops nested within this loop, assign this loop a depth equal to one more than the greatest contained depth. If there are no loops nested within this loop, assign this loop a depth of one.
   b. Let the index variable of this DO loop be i. Count the number of distinct cells referenced within this loop by a subscript dependent on i. This is the number of internal operands.
   c. Whenever a DO loop contains another loop nested within it such that the Boolean relation used to select cells for the inner loop involves a comparison between the contents of two cells, one selected by the outer loop and one a proposed candidate for the inner loop, the mode of address of the outer loop is "tag."
      Whenever within a DO loop that is not of the tag mode of address, a cell in memory is referenced by obtaining its relative displacement from a second cell, the mode of address is "relative."

Whenever a DO loop is neither of tag nor relative mode, it is of a "direct" mode of address.

d. Whenever, within a DO loop, there exist two distinct values of the index variable such that the portion (field) of the memory cell into which the resultant is written for one value of the index serves as an input for the other value of the index, the loop is called "internally coupled."

Whenever, within a DO loop that is not internally coupled, there exists an external variable that is used both to store a resultant and to serve as an input (is both written into and read from), the loop is called "externally coupled." If the operations that refer to this external variable are executable in a character serial mode and are "bubblable," the loop is called symmetrically externally coupled. Otherwise, it is called asymmetrically externally coupled.

Whenever within a DO loop that is neither internally nor externally coupled an inner loop is externally coupled to a variable that is an internal variable of the outer loop, the outer loop is called coupled between levels.

Whenever a DO loop is none of the above, it is called uncoupled.

SUMMARY

In this section, a primitive operation for the ISC is presented, and a set of four descriptors with which to characterize this primitive is developed. It has been shown that these descriptors must be applied to algorithms and not to problems themselves. Finally, some reasons have been presented why these descriptors were chosen.

4 | ELEMENTARY MACHINES

In this chapter we are going to define three primitive machines. Perhaps it would be more accurate to say we are going to discuss three Content Addressable Memories, since we will assume that there is a central processor external to our memory that issues instructions and receives reports about the number of responders.

In one sense these designs are straw men because nobody would ever build a device so limited. In another sense, however, they will serve as calibration points against the descriptors of the previous chapter and against the much more sophisticated designs of the latter chapters.

MACHINE ONE

This is the very simplest of machines that we will consider. In fact, except for Slade and McMahon's cyrotron catalog memory [1], it is probably as simple as has ever been proposed.

The central control unit has a Mask and a Comparand register and receives its instructions from a separate device that will remain unspecified here. Figure 4.1 shows a typical bit and the tag bit of a word. This is almost identical with the machine of Chapter 2, except for the lack of a read circuit.

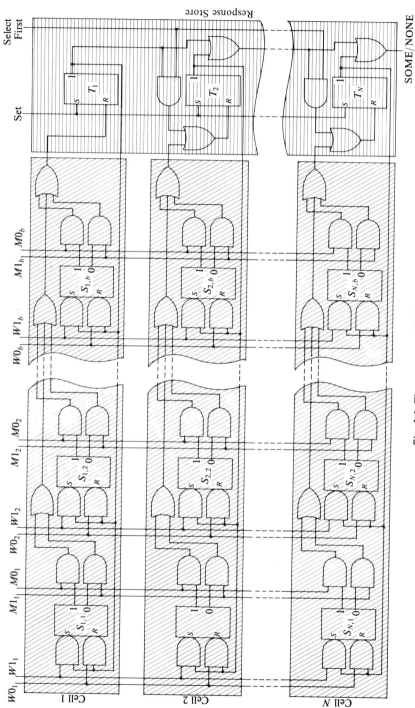

Fig. **4.1** The memory of Machine 1.

The repertoire of instructions that this machine can perform on its Content Addressable Memory section are:

SET   —Turn on all tag bits.

COMPARE—Where the Mask contains *ones* compare the bits of the comparand to the bits of every cell simultaneously. If the comparand and the cell disagree, reset the tag bit of that cell. Where the mask has zeros do not do any comparison.

WRITE   —In those portions of the word where the mask contains *ones*, copy the contents of the Comparand into each cell that is a responder (whose tag bit is *one*). Do not change the state of the response store tag bits. In those portions of the word where the Mask contains *zeros* do not disturb the original values of any of the cells.

FIRST   —Keep the first responder, reset all others.

REPORT   —Tell the control unit if any cells are responders.

Machine 1 can process, in parallel (in a time independent of the number of cells involved) all ISC's that are monadic, directly addressed, depth one, and uncoupled. It is shown below that the proposed instruction set for this machine is both necessary and sufficient for this class and insufficient for any other class.

Necessity

To demonstrate Necessity of these operations, we show that ISC's of this class exist that could not be executed in parallel if any of these instructions were eliminated. Three problems are examined:

1. "Discover if the storage array contains the word:

$$w = w_1 w_2 \ldots w_b,$$

where $w_i = 0, 1$."

2. "Write a ONE in the least significant bit in every cell of the array whose match bits are SET. Make no other changes."

3. "Write a ZERO in every cell. Then write x in one cell and y in another."

That these are all monadic, directly addressed, depth one, uncoupled problems can be shown readily by constructing algorithms to execute them (see Fig. 4.2.)

```
1)      FLAG = 0
        DO 10  I = 1, N
        IF (ARRAY(I) .EQ. W) FLAG = 1
   10 CONTINUE

2)      DO 10  I = 1, N
        IF (TAG(I) .EQ. 1)          Clear low order bit of ARRAY(I)
   10 CONTINUE

3)      DO 10  I = 1, N
        ARRAY(I) = 0
   10 CONTINUE
        ARRAY(1) = X
        ARRAY(2) = Y
```

Fig. 4.2 Three algorithms.

For Problem 1, the comparison must take place in parallel if we are to finish in a time independent of N. This machine provides a way of performing the comparison using COMPARE and REPORT in that order and provides no alternate method. The comparison makes only those words that match the comparand be responders. The Report tells the central control unit if there are any responders or not. Thus, these operations are necessary.

For Problem 2, by the same argument, the WRITE operation must be performed locally, and some form of "modifying operation" must be available to deposit information in the cells. Because WRITE is the only modifying operation available in the instruction set, it is necessary.

Problem 3 illustrates another aspect of computer design. If the machine is not to get "trapped" in some subset of states, there must be a path (sequence of instructions) that will transform the state of the machine from S_i to S_j, where i and j are any two possible machine configurations. Therefore, since COMPARE resets match bits, there must be some operation that reverses this process. SET is the only proposed operation that serves this function and hence is necessary. Note that WRITE modifies only the memory storage bits and does not affect the tag bits.

Problem 3 illustrates directly another possible "trap state." Once two cells are caused to contain the same bit configuration (all ZEROs in this example), it is impossible, using only the other four operations, to cause them to contain different symbols. The only way to make them differ is to write something in one and not in the other.

This can be done with the WRITE operation only if the tag bit of one cell is set and that of the other is reset. But SET sets both of them, and because their contents are identical by assumption, COMPARE resets either both or neither of them. This implies that without a FIRST operation, any machine configuration in which two cells differed would be unreachable from any configuration in which they were the same. Therefore, FIRST is necessary.

Sufficiency

It is shown now that any uncoupled, monadic, directly addressed, depth one iteration of a single simple conditional statement can be executed in parallel in Machine 1.

Without loss of generality, the component of the vector addressed on the ith pass through the loop can be said to be V_i. Note that since the algorithm is monadic, there is only one component addressed on each pass.

The Boolean expression of the ISC will select certain cells for execution of the assignment statement and reject the rest. Any Boolean expression can be stated as a sum of products with one or more terms. The cells selected will be the union of all those cells that satisfy the first condition with those that satisfy the second condition, and so on. We begin by clearing the marker bit q to *zero* in all cells (SET, WRITE $q = 0$). Then for each product term in the Boolean expression, we SET all cells, load mask and comparand with the conditions for meeting this product term, COMPARE, discarding those cells which don't meet this condition, and finally WRITE $q = 1$. After all product terms have been processed, any cell which meets one or more of the conditions is marked with $q = 1$. All other cells have $q = 0$.

The substitution statement Q of the simple conditional can be one of three types:

1. Test if any cells match requirements (set flag).
2. Read out the first matching cell.
3. Execute the statement and store the resultant R_i in V_i.

This is true because this algorithm is uncoupled. No external source can be modified on any pass since, by definition, these sources are common to all passes and, the algorithm being uncoupled, must remain invariant. Therefore, R_i must either be V_i or a register that is not a source. If it is V_i, this is a Type 3 statement. If it is an external register, either it is a "flag" whose contents are ORed into it (Type 1), or, if the contents are gained by replacement, the substitution statement might just as well be executed only on the "last" matching pass since all others will be wiped out. By reordering the passes (which can be done for an uncoupled routine), the last can be called "first," in which case a READ FIRST (Type 2) followed by a single execution of the statement will be sufficient.

Type 1 statements can be executed using just the REPORT operation.

Type 2 statements can be executed by using FIRST and then applying the "read algorithm" shown in Fig. 4.3.

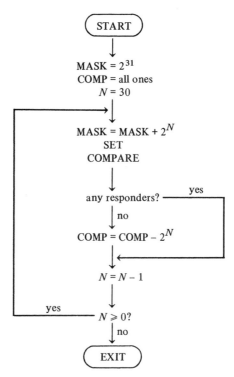

Fig. 4.3 An algorithm for Machine 1 to "read" out the contents of the one cell in the array whose left-most bit is set to one. By "reading out" we mean to obtain a copy of the contents of the cell in the comparand register. N is an index variable stored in the central control unit. The machine is assumed to have a 32-bit word.

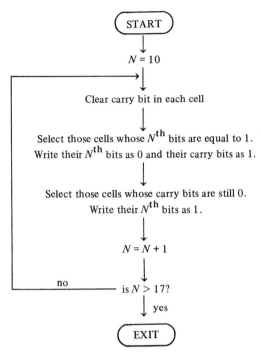

Fig. 4.4 An algorithm to complement bits 10–17 of every cell. The left-most bit of each cell ("carry bit") is used to mark cells as "processed."

Any arithmetic (Type 3) statement executable on a von Neumann computer can be expanded into a string of additions, and complementations. Figure 4.4 shows an algorithm that complements a subset of the bits of all cells. Figure 4.5 shows addition of left half of each word to the right half of the same word. Addition of a constant can easily be handled by repeated addition of one as shown in Chapter 2. This completes the proof.

Comment

Although no explicit statement of monadicity is made above, it is implicit throughout. If, for example, the algorithm were dyadic, it would require at least once that a cell "know" about the state of (or the contents of) some other cell. But there is no machinery in this design to accomplish this for all cells in parallel. By similar argument,

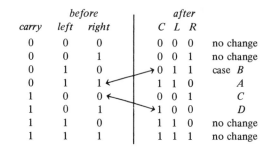

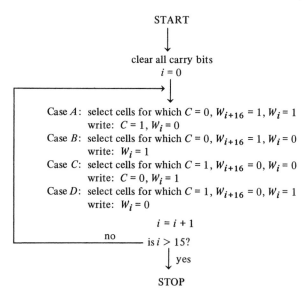

Fig. 4.5 An algorithm to add the left part (bits 30–16) of each cell to the right part (bits 15–0). Bit 31 serves as the carry bit.

relative addressing is ruled out because it would require that a directly selected cell be able to transfer its "activity" to the cell named in its tag field. But again, there is no machinery to accomplish this simultaneously for two cells, let alone n cells. Similar arguments apply to indirect addressing.

As long as an algorithm is monadic, it must be of depth one. Greater depths would require at least two nested iteration statements with two different indexes, each pointing at a component of the vector, thus making it polyadic. Note that in executing an inner loop, we are not concerned with coupling between levels. That affects only the outer loop.

As is seen below in the discussion of Machine 3, more information feedback to central control is required for externally coupled ISC's than is available here. Thus, it can be concluded that Machine 1 cannot execute in parallel externally coupled ISC's.

Internally coupled ISC's are not considered to be adapted for parallel processing.

MACHINE 2

Machine 2 is intended to extend the domain of Machine 1 by eliminating the restriction to monadic ISC's. It is intended to execute in parallel all ISC's that are depth one, uncoupled, and either direct or relative addressed (but not tag addressed). To the repertoire of Machine 1, we add the MOVE instruction which moves activity (set tag bits) north, east, south, or west one position.

Figure 4.6 shows the required hardware assuming that the tag bits in the response store are constructed from master/slave flip-flops

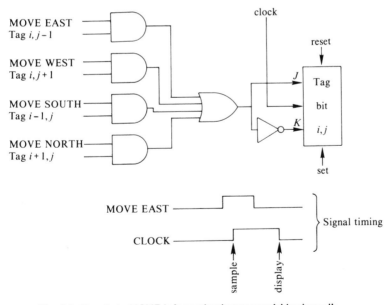

Fig. 4.6 Circuits to MOVE information between neighboring cells.

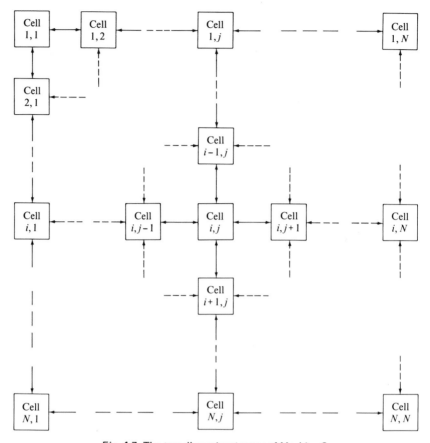

Fig. 4.7 The two dimensional array of Machine 2.

which *absorb* information when the clock line goes high and *display* that information when the clock returns to zero.

Machine 2 consists of an array of cells on a two dimensional grid. Each cell (i, j) can communicate (using the TRANSFER instruction) with four neighbors, the one to the North $(i - 1, j)$, to the East $(i, j + 1)$, to the South $(i + 1, j)$ and to the West $(i, j - 1)$.

Figure 4.7 shows a picture of this array.

Necessity

The necessity of the five instructions that Machine 2 shares with Machine 1 has been shown already. Consideration of the problem:

"Mark each cell (WRITE $q = 1$) if and only if its left-hand neighbor contains zero."

indicates the necessity of some form of intercell communication for polyadic ISC's. This can be expressed as an ISC if we remember that for a two-dimensional array, we can generate a single linear subscript and cell $(i - 1, j)$ can be expressed as cell $(I - N)$ where N is the width of the array. Then

$$\text{For } I = 1, N^2 \text{ IF } X(I - N) = 0 \text{ THEN } Q(I) = 1.$$

The four proposed MOVE instructions are elementary. Only one bit of information is transferred: the state of the tag flip-flop of the appropriate neighbor. Therefore, this instruction is necessary.

Sufficiency

As in the proof for Machine 1, the ability to express the Boolean relation as a sum of products points the way to a scheme for Machine 2's evaluation. Assume that all internal operands of a given pass are lined up next to each other in a single row (which will be justified below). Suppose there are 10 internal operands for each pass and each is stored in a different word: $i, 1; i, 2; \ldots ; i, 9$.

Now select the first product term of the Boolean expression. Suppose it applies to internal operands 2, 3, and 7, for example. Let there be a bit (q) reserved in the first cell of each row to serve as a flag for that row, and let each cell have two fields I and J which hold that cell's location on the grid. Select all cells with J field equal to 7. (That is the seventh cell in each row). Compare the data fields of these cells with the criterion specified by this product term for internal operand 7. Discard (make non-responders) those which do not meet this criterion. Now MOVE activity Westward (to the left) 4 times. In each row for which internal operand 7 was "right" we will have as a responder that row's 3rd internal operand. Now match against the criterion specified by this product term for internal operand 3. We are left with responders (in the 3rd column) of exactly those rows for which both the 3rd and the 7th internal operands were "right." MOVE West one space the remaining sparks of activity. Repeat the match on the criterion for internal operand 2. Move activity West once more (into column 1) and write $q = 1$ in the first cells of those rows that met all the criteria of the first product term. Repeat the whole operation for each product term. The result will be a $q = 1$ in each row which met the criteria of one or more of the product terms, as desired.

As before, there are three kinds of substitution statements for polyadic ISC's that are uncoupled.

As before, add and complement are the only two operations required to execute an arithmetic algorithm, and these must be applied between any two cells.

It is shown first that if all passes through the loop have the same geometric layout of operands (as was assumed above), it is possible (1) to add the contents of any two cells and store the result in a third cell (see Fig. 4.8), and (2) to complement the contents of any

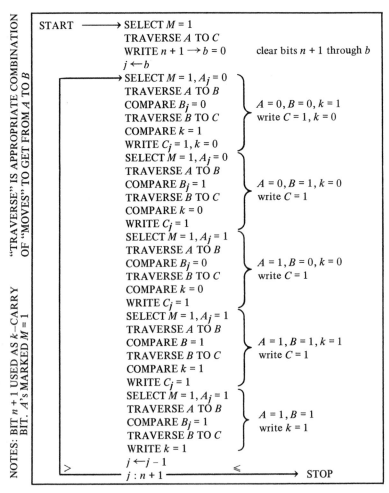

Fig. 4.8 Algorithm to Add Contents of A and B and Store Result in C.

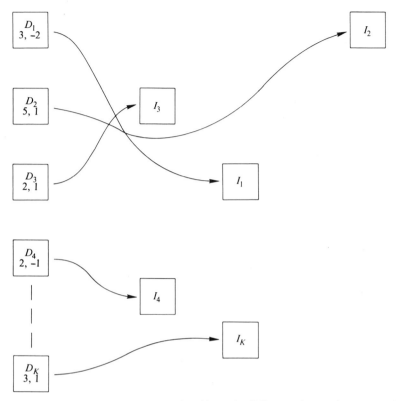

Fig. 4.9 Relative addressing. Each directly addressed cell D_j contains a pointer to another cell I_j which contains the desired data.

cell under control of any other. This algorithm is left as an exercise for the reader. The pseudo operation TRAVERSE A to B is intended to stand for the necessary combination of MOVES required to turn on Cell B_j if Cell A_j was on to start with.

It has been assumed so far that all passes have the same geometric layout of operands. But if relative addressing is desired, the relative coordinates of the desired data cell are stored in the tag fields or pointers of the directly addressed cells.

Let the contents of the directly addressed cell specify the geometric relationship of the desired cell to itself. Anthropomorphically then, it might say: "Not me! Go three to the right and down six. There's the one you want!" Each directly addressed cell might contain different directions. (See Fig. 4.9). A process that will retrieve these indirectly addressed data is shown below.

The directly addressed cells ("*D*-cells") will be in a regular array, and their pointers must be replaced by the data in the tag-addressed cell.

Messengers

The following algorithm is due to Fanya Montalvo of the University of Massachusetts. We wish to present a scheme whereby each active cell (*D*) can send out a "messenger" that will gradually make its way to its destination (*I*). There it will pick up information and then carry it home. If we can do this we can execute any polyadic algorithm.

For simplicity we assume that no two active cells wish to retrieve data from the same destination. We will also assume that all messengers will work their way outbound and then wait. After everyone reaches their destinations, we will send all the messengers off on their homeward journey.

To perform this algorithm we assume that every cell in memory is divided into three fields. The first and largest of these fields is called the private field which contains data that is not moving. The two remaining fields *B* and *C* constitute the messenger space. On the outward journey *B* contains the directions of how to get home and *C* contains the distance still to be traversed before the destination is reached. On the return journey *B* contains the data to be carried home and *C* the distance yet to cover. Distance will be stored in two subfields called *X* and *Y*, and will be in twos complement notation with North and East being the positive directions. (Yes, this was written in New England. How did you guess?) When a messenger reaches its destination it will be "withdrawn" into the private field so that traffic can continue to pass through the *BC* fields.

We begin with a lot of messengers scattered about the array (see Fig. 4.10). There are two basic parts to the algorithm: *moving* North and South, and *forcing* East and West. Consider first the moving North. If a messenger with positive *Y* (one that wishes to move North) is below an empty cell, we move that messenger one square North. If the cell above contains another messenger that wishes to move South ($Y < 0$) we interchange the two and both are closer to their goals. If a North seeking cell is below a cell for which $Y \geqslant 0$, it waits. If the cell above it also is North seeking ($Y > 0$) that messenger will eventually move away and this messenger can move (we

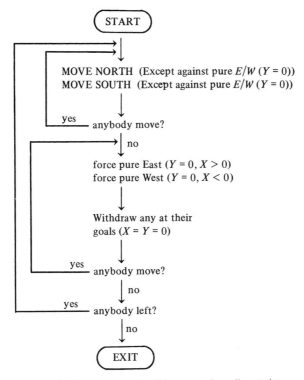

START

MOVE NORTH (Except against pure E/W ($Y = 0$))
MOVE SOUTH (Except against pure E/W ($Y = 0$))

yes

anybody move?

no

force pure East ($Y = 0, X > 0$)
force pure West ($Y = 0, X < 0$)

Withdraw any at their
goals ($X = Y = 0$)

yes

anybody move?

no

yes

anybody left?

no

EXIT

Fig. 4.10 The messenger algorithm to retrieve distant data.

prove this later). If the blocking cell has $Y = 0$, it is a "pure-East-Wester" and we take care of that below.

Moving South is just the reverse of moving North. Note in particular that after sufficient cycles of moving North and South (when nobody can move any more) it is guaranteed that in every non-empty column there will be at least one messenger with $Y = 0$; that is, a messenger that has "gotten home" or else has become a "pure-East Wester". (See Fig. 4.11.)

Now we enter the second phase and *force* messengers to move East and West. We treat only those messengers that are on their home row ($Y = 0$) and we consider five cases as shown in Fig. 4.12.

In case *a* where a messenger wishes to move into an empty cell, it does, provided somebody else doesn't get there first. In case *b* where a pure-East-Wester wants to move into a cell occupied by a messenger that needs to move North or South, these two messengers are inter-

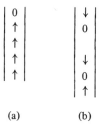

(a)   (b)

Fig. 4.11 Several sample columns in which the value of Y is displayed as an arrow or a 0 depending on its sign and magnitude. X, the horizontal component, is not considered here.

	before		after	
a)	→ empty		empty →	
b)	→ ↕		↕ →	
c)	→ ←		← →	
d)	→ 0		→ empty	
e)	→ → empty		→ empty →	

Fig. 4.12 The cases to be considered during the "force East West" phase of the algorithm. The symbol ↕ is to be interpreted as a messenger with a non-zero Y component and an unspecified X component. The symbols →, ←, and 0 indicate messengers with $Y = 0$ and respectively East-seeking, West-seeking, and "at home."

changed (and their X subfields updated.). The pure Easter (shown) moves one step closer to its goal and the North-Souther may move closer to its goal or further away. In case c a pure Easter faces a pure Wester and after interchange both are better off. In case d where an East desiring messenger faces a cell whose messenger is "at home", we don't move the cell that is at home, but during this iteration the "at home" messenger will be withdrawn. Finally, in case e the East desiring messengers that are behind other East-seeking cells wait but the right-most one does move out.

In summary, in every case (except when somebody is already at home and is temporarily blocking movement) each iteration of "force East West" moves somebody (in each column that contains pure-East-Westers) closer to their goal. Thus, after a finite number of cycles, at least one pure-East-West messenger (in each row containing *any* pure-East-Westers) will get home. But the move North-South algorithm guarantees that in any non-empty column we will have a pure-East-Wester. It is clear then that after a finite number of passes through the algorithm of Fig. 4.9 all the messengers will get home.

The reader should note two important points. First, all messengers are considered in parallel simultaneously. Thus the time required for each pass through the North-South loop and the East-West loop is independent of the number of messengers. Secondly, our logic guarantees that at least one messenger will become a pure-East-Wester per non-empty column (for the North-South loop) or at least one messenger per non-empty row will get home (for the East-West loop). The good Lord, and Mr. Euclid willing, performance will average considerably better than this minimum.

MACHINE 3

Machine 3 is just like machine 1 except that it can count the number of responders in a time independent of the size of the memory. This counting operation can replace the REPORT function of machine 1 so the set of instructions executable on this machine are:

SET
COMPARE
WRITE
FIRST

and

COUNT—tell the control unit how many responders there are.

If there are N cells in the memory then the count will consist of a binary number with

$$b = \lceil \log_2 N \rceil$$

bits in it. One obvious, but expensive, way of generating this count would be to have b two level circuits, with N inputs each, that would generate the bits of the count. Other, less Neanderthalic approaches are discussed in Chapter 7.

Given machine 3, we can execute in parallel all ISC's that are monadic, directly addressed, depth one, and symmetrically externally coupled or else uncoupled.

Necessity

Consider the following problem: "Count the number of positive words in the array." in FORTRAN

```
        COUNT = 0
        DO  10  I = 1, N
        IF  (A(I).GE.0) COUNT = COUNT + 1
  10    CONTINUE
```

This is clearly monadic and symmetrically externally coupled. Also clearly, it can't be done in time independent of N unless some kind of COUNT instruction is available.

Sufficiency

At first blush it is not obvious that all symetrically externally coupled ISC's can be processed by a COUNT instruction. But if we look back at the definition of symmetric, we find that it means that in each column (bit-slice) of the array all the *ones* can be bubbled to one end of the array and all the *zeros* to the other end. Given that we have done this, nothing is left except the number of *ones,* no other information about where they were. So we can conclude that indeed the COUNT instruction is sufficient for symmetrically externally coupled ISC's.

SUMMARY

We have defined three primitive machines. Many others could have been defined. We chose a set that would fit in with our descriptors of the previous chapter. Readers are urged to consider the interacting problems of primitive machines and descriptors and treat these two chapters as only a zeroth order approximation to a useful set.

5 | ALGORITHMS

The algorithms for CAPP's divide neatly into two classes: those that are looking for a class of responders, and those that are doing something to a class of responders. The obvious temptation, to which we will succumb, is to call the first type "logical" and the second "arithmetic."

We will deal with the logical algorithms first, and then later with the arithmetic. In each case we will begin by displaying an algorithm in the form which requires the least amount of special hardware. Then we will examine what arrangement of gates and auxilliary flip-flops will give us the maximum possible speed of execution. Throughout this chapter, we will reserve certain bits of each cell to serve as "flag" bits. In different algorithms, we will use them differently.

LOGICAL ALGORITHMS

The basic article describing logical algorithms for CAM's is the one by Falkoff, 1962. He presents most of the algorithms of this class and he uses APL to describe them. Other papers discussing general algorithms include Estrin, 1963b, Foster, 1970a, and Fuller, 1963. We will review them here for completeness.

There are a number of ways of categorizing logical algorithms. One can, as Falkoff did, distinguish between those that have constant argument (comparand) and those with variable argument. We will present some of each below. From a design point of view, however, there is not a great deal of difference whether the comparand register gets changed or not.

A second aspect of algorithms is the question whether or not parallel-by-bit searches would speed up the operation of the algorithm. This is more important. As we will see below, some algorithms that are serial-by-bit take $4N$ steps (N is the number of bits searched) while other algorithms to accomplish the same task take $N^2/2$ steps if executed bit serially. But these latter algorithms take N steps if bit-parallel operation is available. All algorithms will be done bit-serially unless otherwise specified. This means compare one bit at a time (in every cell, of course) or write one bit at a time (again in every cell).

As this is written, it appears that semiconductor memories will be the technology ultimately used to build CAM's. Given pin limitation of chips and given the desire for long words in the CAM, it seems reasonable to predict that bit-serial approaches will be the ones most likely to be useful. We will however, present some of each.

Finally, one can divide algorithms into those which require feedback from the array as to how they are doing, and those which don't; that is, whether or not they use the "report" function to tell the central control unit if there are any responders. In the "damn the torpedoes" class we have exact match, compare, and many arithmetic algorithms, whereas the "every step with caution feeling" group includes find maximum, minimum, next larger, and next smaller.

Let us begin with the standard exact match search just to demonstrate the way we are going to approach things and for the sake of those who have skipped chapter 2.

Exact Match

We wish to compare all candidates (not all cells may be candidates) with the contents of the Comparand Register. Where the Mask Register holds zeros, we will not do a comparison; but where it holds ones, we will insist that the bit of the comparand C_j and the bit of the word $W_{i,j}$ are the same. We will in general ignore the Mask Register, assuming that it has done its task so well that only the "interesting" bits are coming up for consideration.

We begin with all the cells in the "undecided" state (with their response store bit R set to *one*) and as we go through the bits of interest whenever we find $C_j W_{i,j} = 10$ or 01 we "discard" (mark as a non-responder) the cell. (See Fig. 5.1.) After all bits are examined,

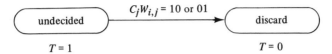

Fig. 5.1 A cell-state transition diagram for the exact match search.

those cells left in the "undecided" state are exact matches with the comparand and those in the "discard" state are the mismatches plus whatever cells were not originally candidates.

Figure 5.2 shows a flow diagram of this algorithm. It is clear that

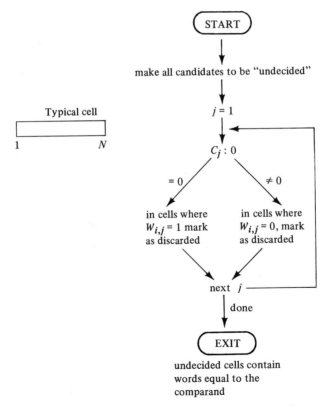

Fig. 5.2 A flow diagram of the algorithm for exact match.

this algorithm could be executed in bit-serial or bit-parallel mode, and that in serial mode it could be executed either left to right or right to left. We will seldom find this much flexibility. What we have here is an algorithm whose repetitive loop can be realized temporally (bit-serial) or spatially (bit-parallel). Executed in bit-parallel, it requires one probe of the memory to set words undecided and one probe to do the search. In bit-serial, it requires $N + 1$ probes; one for each of N bits to COMPARE each bit, plus an initial probe to set all cells into the undecided state.

In Fig. 5.3, we assume that some unspecified means are available to present the bits of the word $W_{i,j}$ as required. This might imply that the memory cell can function as a shift register or it might mean that addressing logic within the cell will develop $W_{i,j}$ when given the bit number j.

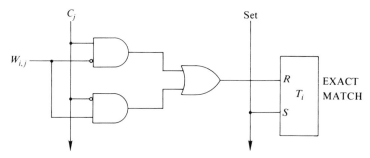

Fig. 5.3 Circuit designed for bit serial exact match search. All candidates initially have Response Store bit T SET and the discard state is represented by having T turned off. Some form of bit addressing logic causes the jth bit of each cell to present its value at W_j.

Mismatch

Several variations on mismatch can be defined: comparand and word differ in every bit position (exact mismatch) or in some bit positions, or in some but not all, and so forth. In the opinion of this author, these are not terribly interesting, and further, they can be derived in an obvious fashion from the exact match search.

Question 5.1: Design algorithms for each of these definitions of mismatch.

A mismatch algorithm that is more interesting is what we shall call the quantized mismatch. In this search, we will keep track of the number of bits that mismatch the comparand and eventually select the cell with the fewest mismatches. This algorithm will be discussed in detail below, but is mentioned here for completeness.

Compare Magnitude with Comparand

Several algorithms exist to sort the words of memory into classes of greater than, greater than or equal to, less than, less than or equal to, and of course, equal and not equal to. Rather than go through all the variations, we will present one algorithm which divides the words into three classes: less than, equal to, and greater than the comparand. We use three flag bits for this algorithm, called XYZ.

We assume for simplicity that all numbers are positive. This is equivalent to assuming that positive numbers are represented with sign bit of *one* and negative numbers with sign bit of *zero*. This is sometimes called "excess 2^N arithmetic." This algorithm is presented in Fig. 5.4. The three states that a word can be in are shown

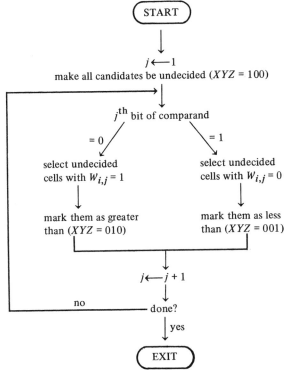

Fig. 5.4 Algorithm to divide cells of memory into three classes depending on their magnitude compared with the comparand. Excess 2^n integers.

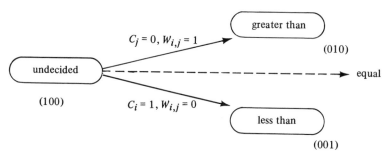

Fig. 5.5 State transition diagram for cells in the compare algorithm with flag assignment shown in parentheses.

in Fig. 5.5. Initially, all words are made "undecided." ($XYZ = 100$) This takes four probes to accomplish (SET, WRITE $X = 1$, WRITE $Y = 0$, WRITE $Z = 0$). Note that this assumes writing is done one bit at a time in all cells of memory. At the end of the algorithm, words still in this state are equal to the comparand. Bits are scanned from most significant to least significant. Whenever the bit of the comparand C_j is *zero*, we select all undecided words (SET, COMPARE for $X = 1$) with a *one* ($W_{i,j} = 1$) (COMPARE $C_j = 1$) and mark them as "decided greater than." That is we will make their flag bits contain $XYZ = 010$. This requires two more probes (WRITE $X = 0$, WRITE $Y = 1$) for a total of five. Conversely, when C_j is one, we make undecided words with *zero* ($W_{i,j} = 0$) "decided less than." ($XYZ = 001$). For each bit position this also takes five probes. This results in $5N + 4$ probes assuming three bits are used for flags.

With multi-bit COMPAREs and WRITEs, the timing is $3N + 2$. The algorithm could be designed to use only two flags XY with assignments

$$10 - \text{equal or undecided}$$
$$01 - \text{greater than}$$
$$00 - \text{less than}$$

Assuming half the bits of the comparand are *zero* and half are *one*, this takes $4\frac{1}{2} N + 4$ probes because only one bit needs to be changed to mark words as less than, whereas two must be changed in going from "undecided" to "greater than." On the other hand, using three flag bits as shown, we have XYZ

$$010 - \text{greater than}$$

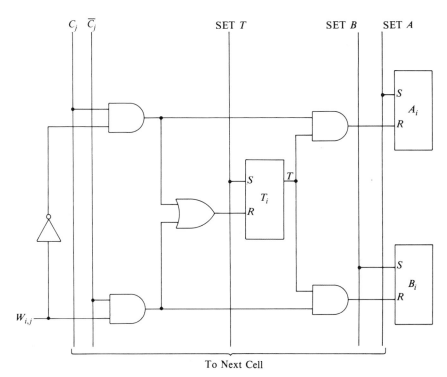

Fig. 5.6 Special hardware to carry out the "compare with comparand" algorithm in $N + 1$ probes.

100—equal or undecided
001—less than

and can for example conveniently choose words greater than or equal to the comparand by selecting those with $Z = 0$.

Using the special hardware shown in Fig. 5.6, we can tricotomize the memory in $N + 1$ probes, the one being needed to *set R, A*, and *B* simultaneously, initially. Any mismatch between the comparand and the word will reset R but the delay in passing through the OR gate and the flip-flop R will allow us to also clear the appropriate one of A or B depending on the "kind" of mismatch.

If we wish to deal with conventional two's complement numbers which have negative sign of *one* and positive sign of *zero*, we simply reverse the sense of the test on the first bit. (See Fig. 5.7) Such a comparison algorithm is left as an exercise for the reader.

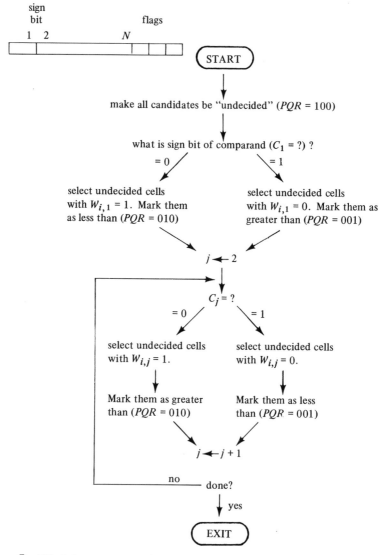

Fig. 5.7 A three-way comparison algorithm for two's complement integers.

Five-Way Split

The following algorithm was originally proposed by Wolinsky, 1969, and expanded here by the present author.

Suppose we have two numbers called UPPER and LOWER, and we wish to find those words of memory that are greater than LOWER but less than UPPER. This is called a "between limits" search and the standard method of carrying it out is to concatenate a search for greater-than-LOWER with a search for less-than-UPPER. Wolinsky showed a method that in one pass across the words would divide memory into those words greater-than-UPPER, between-UPPER-

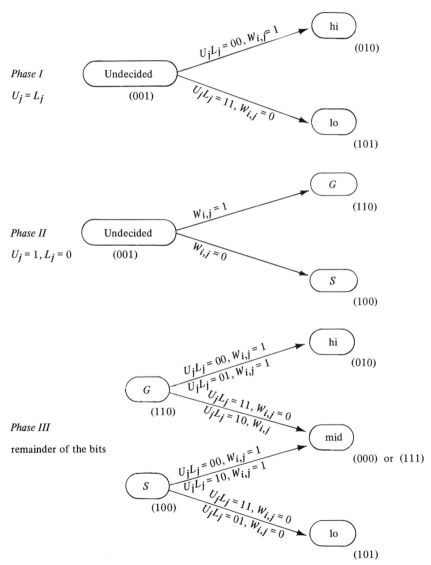

Fig. 5.8 The three phases of the five-way split cell-state assignment transitions.

and-LOWER, and less-than-LOWER. The present author added the categories: equal-to-UPPER and equal-to-LOWER, making it a five-way split.

Figure 5.8 shows the cell-state transitions, and the state assignments (flag patterns) we have chosen. Bits are scanned left to right. The algorithm has three phases. The first phase lasts as long as the two comparands are identical. (See Fig. 5.9). If both U_j and L_j are

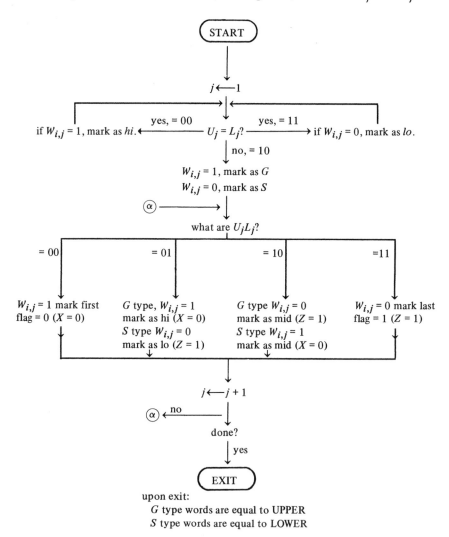

Fig. 5.9 Flow diagram for the algorithm for the five-way split.

one then for undecided cells with $W_{i,j} = 0$ we know they are less than lower so we convert 001 to 101 (type "Lo"). Conversely, undecided cells with $W_{i,j} = 1$ when $U_j = L_j = 0$ can convert directly to type "Hi." The second phase of the algorithm is applied to only one bit; the left-most bit where UPPER and LOWER differ. Since, by definition, UPPER is greater than LOWER, we have $U_j = 1$ and $L_j = 0$. In this phase all remaining undecided words are converted to type "G" or type "S" depending on whether $W_{i,j} = 1$ or $W_{i,j} = 0$, respectively.

The third phase is carried out over all remaining bits of the comparands. For each value of j, U_j and L_j take on one of four possible sets of values. Depending on which set they assume, we enter one of four subroutines. If $U_j L_j = 00$, then if the G or S word has a *one* in this position ($W_{i,j} = 1$) we know that it is greater than that bound ($G >$ UPPER and $L >$ LOWER). Given our stated assignment, we make the first flag bit *zero*, thus converting $G(110)$ to $Hi(010)$ and $S(100)$ to $Mid(000)$. If $U_j L_j = 11$ and $W_{i,j} = 0$, we change the last bit of the flag to *one* making $G(110)$ become $Mid(111)$ and $S(100)$ become $Lo(101)$. If $U_j L_j = 01$ then G-type words with $W_{i,j} = 0$ become Mid and S-type words with $W_{i,j} = 1$ also become Mid. Figure 5.8 shows this in flow diagram form.

In phase I we need four probes to identify undecided words (SET, COMPARE $X = 0$, COMPARE $Y = 0$, COMPARE $Z = 1$) and one probe to find the $W_{i,j}$ and $1\frac{1}{2}$ probes to change the flags (WRITE $Y = 1$, WRITE $Z = 0$ if the change is to Hi and WRITE $X = 1$ if the change is to Lo) for a total of $6\frac{1}{2}$ probes per bit. (See Fig. 5.10.)

In phase II, we need five probes to select undecided with $W_{i,j} = 1$ (SET, COMPARE $X = 0$, COMPARE $Y = 0$, COMPARE $Z = 1$, COMPARE $W_{i,j} = 1$) and then three to mark them as type G (WRITE $X = 1$, WRITE $Y = 1$, WRITE $Z = 0$) plus five more probes to select undecided with $W_{i,j} = 0$ and one (WRITE $X = 1$) to convert undecided (001) to S-type (101). This gives a total of 14 probes for phase II.

In phase III, we may assume that half the time U_j and L_j agree. This case needs three probes to get the type G and S words (SET, COMPARE $X = 1$, COMPARE $Z = 0$), one to get the right value of $W_{i,j}$, and one to change the bit of the flag for a total of five. When U_j and L_j disagree, we need five probes to select the type G with correct $W_{i,j}$ (SET, COMPARE $X = 1$, COMPARE $Y = 1$, COMPARE $Z = 1$, COMPARE $W_{i,j} = ?$) and one probe to change the state

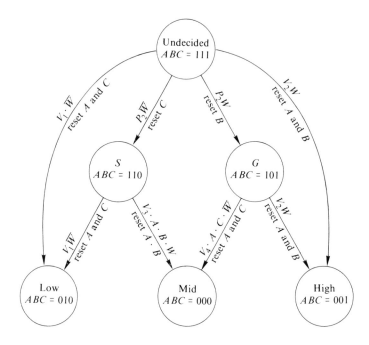

V_1—phase 1 or 3 and $L = 1$
V_2—phase 1 or 3 and $U = 0$
V_3—phase 3 and $L = 0$
V_4—phase 3 and $U = 1$
P_2—phase 2

Fig. 5.10 State transition table for the fast five-way split algorithm. Variables P_2 and V_1 – V_4 are broadcast from central control. Note that the state assignment differs from the slow algorithm.

(WRITE $X = 0$ or WRITE $Z = 1$) plus the same number to fix up the S-type words. This gives twelve probes. Assuming equality and difference occur equally often, phase III takes an average of $8\frac{1}{2}$ probes per bit. Taking the worst case of zero length phase I, we have $8\frac{1}{2} N + 14$ probes for the actual algorithm plus four for initializing the flags, plus seven to convert 000 (SET, COMPARE $X = 0$, COMPARE $Y = 0$, COMPARE $Z = 0$, WRITE $X = 1$, WRITE $Y = 1$, WRITE $Z = 1$) to 111 so that all *Mid* type words have the same flag state or a grand total of $8\frac{1}{2} N + 25$ probes.

Other state assignments are possible. Some of them may require fewer probes than this one. Separation of non-candidates can be done at the end of the algorithm on the basis of yet another flag bit.

Question 5.2: Rework this algorithm assuming COMPARES and WRITES of several bits at a time are possible. How long does it take?

Question 5.3: Try some other states of the flag bits. Perhaps four or more flag bits would lead to a simpler algorithm.

The special hardware needed for this classification is reasonably formidable. One version of such hardware is shown in Fig. 5.11.

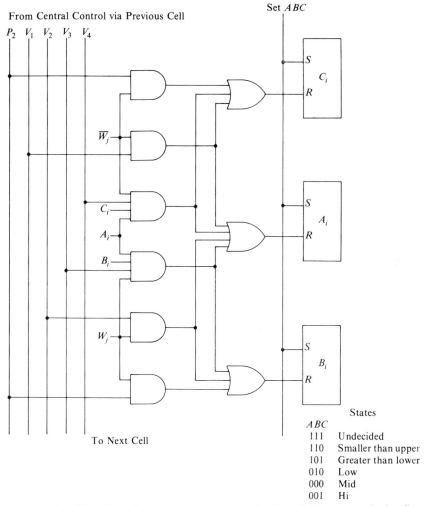

Fig. 5.11 Special hardware in the response store of each cell needed to execute the fast five-way split algorithm.

Algorithms with Feedback

Four algorithms fall into the class in to which feedback from memory is required. The action taken by these algorithms will depend upon whether or not there are any responders at certain times. Therefore, they must utilize the REPORT function. All are variations of the extremum search. They are maximum, minimum, next below, next above. Consider first the search for maximum.

Maximum   We scan bits from left to right, most to least significant. All words begin as candidates.

As we work through the bits we ask if *any* of the candidates ($X = 1$) have a *one* in the current position. If they do, we discard (mark as non-candidates) all those words which don't have a one here. At any given instant, all remaining candidates are equal as far as we have examined them. This is true because for every bit position either everybody had a *zero* in that bit position, or whenever some words have *ones*, we discard the zeros. Therefore, when we look at bit j, undecided words with $W_{i,j} = 1$ are larger than those with $W_{i,j} = 0$. Since we are looking for the maximum word we keep only the largest. Figure 5.12 shows the state diagram and 5.13 shows the flow diagram.

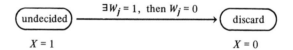

Fig. 5.12 State diagram for finding the maximum.

Question 5.4: Time this algorithm assuming single bit COMPAREs and WRITEs; assuming multiple bit COMPAREs and WRITEs.

The search for minimum is exactly the same except that if any undecided words have $W_{i,j} = 0$, we discard those with $W_{i,j} = 1$. (See Fig. 5.14.)   If we assume that our machine has a "write in Non-Responders" instruction, (See later in this chapter), we need three probes to select undecided words with $W_{i,j} = 1$ (SET, COMPARE $X = 1$, COMPARE $W_{i,j} = 1$) and one more probe to mark non-responders (those with *zero*) as discarded. This requires $4N$ probes

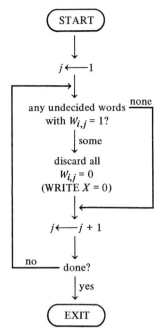

Fig. 5.13 Flow diagram for algorithm to find the maximum word in the array.

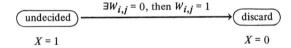

Fig. 5.14 State diagram of algorithm for finding the minimum.

plus two initial probes (SET, WRITE $X = 1$) to mark all words as undecided for a total of $4N + 2$ probes. For multi-bit WRITE and COMPARE this reduces to $3N + 2$. We assume that it takes zero time to determine if there are any responders.

___

Question 5.5: This timing is not, strictly speaking, accurate. Why not?

___

Figure 5.15 shows some hardware that will aid in the search for a maximum. T_i is *one* if the word i is still undecided. We gate $W_{i,j}$ into B_i where T_i is *one*. Then if some T_i is *one* (REPORT) we reset

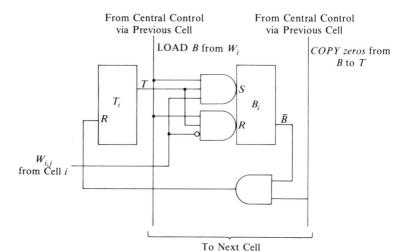

Fig. 5.15 Hardware at the response store of each cell to find the maximum.

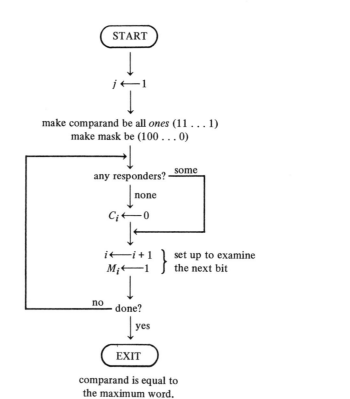

comparand is equal to
the maximum word.

Fig. 5.16 Variable comparand search for maximum. C_j is the jth bit of the comparand.

the T's where $W_{i,j}$ was zero. This takes $2N + 2$ cycles to search over N bits.

There is a variable comparand search for maximum which requires no flags in the words but must have parallel by bit access to run acceptably fast. This algorithm is shown in Fig. 5.16. This requires the order of N probes of memory for bit parallel access and the order of N^2 probes for bit serial access.

Question 5.6: Time these two algorithms.

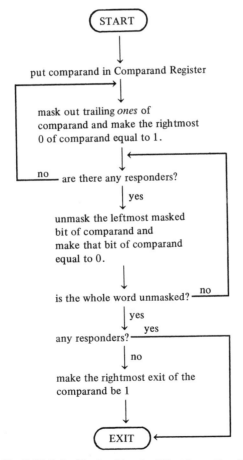

Fig. 5.17 Falkoff's algorithm for "Next larger than."

Next Above   One way to find the word which is the smallest-word-larger-than-the-comparand (the "next above" or "next larger") is to search for those words larger than the comparand and then select the minimum of these. Another, and more interesting approach, is one suggested by Falkoff, 1962. This algorithm is shown in Fig. 5.17. To understand what is going on, consider also Fig. 5.18. Suppose the two words in the square boxes are in memory and 0011 is the comparand.

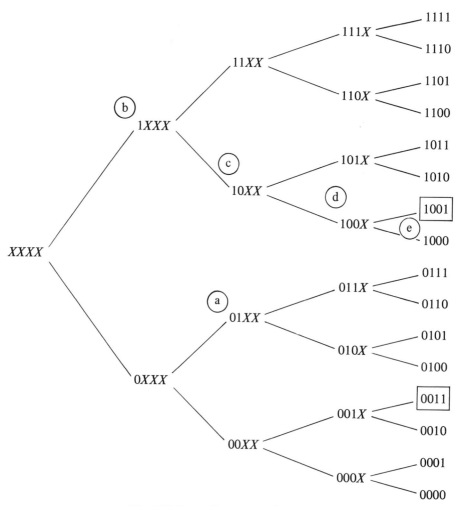

Fig. 5.18 Binary Number Tree à la Falkoff.

First, we mask out trailing *ones* (the search argument is then 00*XX*) and make the rightmost exposed *zero* of the comparand be a *one* (01*XX*). This is point ⓐ . There are no responders to a search for this comparand so we mask off the least significant bit of the comparand (getting 0*XXX*) and change the right-most exposed *zero* to be a *one*. This brings us to point ⓑ (1*XXX*). Now we get some responders, so we unmask another digit and make it a *zero*. The search argument is now 10*XX* or point ⓒ . Again, we get responders, so we go to point ⓓ (100*X*). Still, we have responders, so we go to ⓔ (1000) where there are no responders. Therefore, we convert the rightmost bit to a one (1001) and exit with the comparand register equal to the next larger word. In other words, we climb up the tree until we get a responder and then we descend again, always trying the lower branch first, until the desired word is completely specified.

If we have parallel by bit (multi-bit WRITE and COMPARE) access to N bit words, we need the order of $2N$ probes to discover the word. We go upwards at most $N - 2$ levels and back down $N - 1$. If on the other hand, we have only bit serial access, we examine $N - 1$, $N - 2, \ldots, 2, 1, 2, 3, \ldots, N$ bits. This adds up to $N^2 - 1$ probes in all. For N greater than five or six this is uncomfortably large.

ARITHMETIC ALGORITHMS

In this section we are going to consider several algorithms that form the backbone of the claim of CAPPs to be parallel processors. These basic arithmetic algorithms include one's complement, two's complement, add one, add constant, and add fields. Subtraction algorithms are obvious transformations of the addition algorithms displayed so we will show only the subtract fields algorithm, trusting that our readers can manage the others. While most conventional computers have only addition *or* subtraction circuits and rely on taking the complement of one of the operands in order to carry out the inverse operation, CAPP algorithms are already so slow that it would seem worthwhile to include both types. Multiplication and division are discussed and algorithms are included.

For these arithmetic algorithms, we will assume two's complement representation of negative numbers.

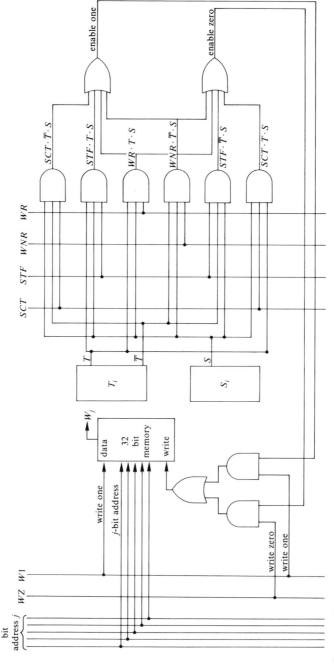

Fig. 5.19 One cell of the expanded CAPP designed for single bit WRITE or COMPARE, including the T and S response store flip-flops and the gates to generate "enable one" or "enable zero."

Revised Hardware

In order to make the various algorithms presented in this section run as fast as possible, we are going to propose a somewhat more complicated version of the machine originally described in Chapter 2. Figure 5.19 shows one cell of this new machine designed for bit parallel operation. Figure 5.20 shows the same design for strictly bit serial operation (WRITE and COMPARE one bit per cell at a time.)

These changes allow us to perform four different writing operations. T is the response store "tag bit" and S is the response store "select bit."

> WR—write into responders. For all cells that are responders ($T = 1$) and that are selected. ($S = 1$) the contents of the masked comparand will be stored in the cell. The mask and comparand will determine whether WZ_j, $W1_j$, or neither are energized for each bit position.
>
> WNR—write into nonresponders. As above, except that only cells for which $T = 0, S = 1$, are written into.
>
> STF—store T (response store) flip-flops. For words that are selected, ($S = 1$) the contents of the T-flip-flops will be stored in each bit position for which $WZ_j = W1_j = 1$. If only $W1_j = 1$, then only *ones* from T are stored—equivalent to an OR operation.

Question 5.7: Why?

> If only $WZ_j = 1$ then only *zeros* from R are stored; equivalent to an AND operation.

Question 5.8: Why?

> If neither $W1_j$ nor WZ_j equal *one* the bit of the cell is unchanged.
>
> SNT—store complement of T. As above, except that the complement of T is used instead of T.

For example, to make $W_{i,j} = 1$ in responders, we would energize $W1_j$ and WR. This would then write *ones* in bit j of those cells with

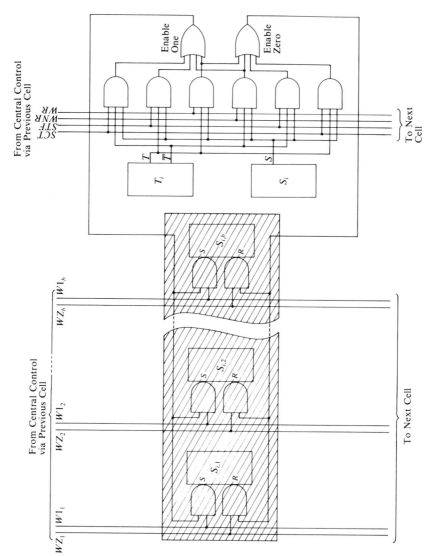

Fig. 5.20 One cell of a CAPP with expanded WRITE control circuits designed for multi-bit WRITE.

$T_i = S_i = 1$. To write *one* in non-responders, we energize $W1_j$ and *WNR*. This would write *one* into bit j of cells with $S_i = 1$, $T_i = 0$. To write zeros we would energize WZ_j instead of $W1_j$. To store the response store into all candidates we energize write one $j(W1_j)$, write zero $j(WZ_j)$ and *STF*. Then in cells with $S_i = 1$, we set $W_{i,j} = 1$ if $T_i = 1$ and $W_{i,j} = 0$ if $T_i = 0$.

Because it turns out to be very useful, we include a *SCT* which permits us to store the complement of T.

One's Complement

For all candidates we wish to replace every *one* with a *zero*, and vice versa. For this particular algorithm, it doesn't matter if we go left to right or the other way. To conform with other arithmetic operations, we will go right to left. To carry out this algorithm (see Fig. 5.21), in our simple memory of Chapter 2 we need two flag bits;

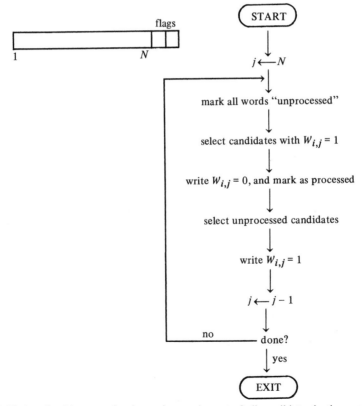

Fig. 5.21 An algorithm to take the one's complement of all candidates in the machine of Chapter 2.

one to indicate the candidates for complementation (X) and one to indicate that a particular bit has been processed (Y).

First we select all words and mark them as unprocessed (SET, WRITE $Y = 0$) then we take candidates with $W_{i,j} = 1$ (COMPARE $X = 1$, COMPARE $W_{i,j} = 1$) and mark them as processed and write $W_{i,j} = 0$ (WRITE $W_{i,j} = 0$, WRITE $Y = 1$). Now all candidates have $W_{i,j} = 0$. Therefore we select unprocessed candidates (SET, COMPARE $X = 1$, COMPARE $Y = 0$) and in these we write $W_{i,j} = 1$. This takes 11 memory probes per bit for a total of $11N$ probes. Using just the ability to selectively write in non-responders and to keep track of which cells contain candidates in the S register, we can revise this algorithm as shown in Fig. 5.22. This takes three probes per bit, more than three times as fast as the machine of Chapter 2.

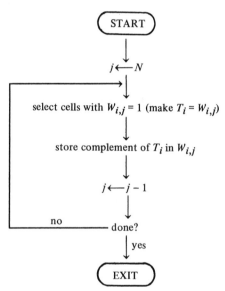

Fig. 5.22 A faster algorithm to take one's complements using the hardware of Fig. 5.19 and for forming the one's complement.

Add One

This algorithm will add one to every candidate in the memory. As we examine the jth bit, four possibilities exist. The bit may be *zero* or *one* and the carry bit may be *zero* or *one*. If the carry bit is *zero* nothing needs to be done. If carry is *one* then for words with $W_{i,j} = 0$ ($W_{i,j}C_i = 01$) we must write $W_{i,j}C_i = 10$. If $W_{i,j} = 1$ ($W_{i,j}C_i = 11$) we must write $W_{i,j}C_i = 01$.

Question 5.9: Does the order of doing this matter?

Figure 5.23 shows the state transitions and 5.24 the flow diagram for the memory of chapter 2. One bit is needed to mark candidates X and one to hold the carry C. This takes eleven steps per bit for a total of $11N + 3$ probes of memory. Using the hardware of Fig. 5.19

Fig. 5.23 Cell state transitions for the add one algorithm.

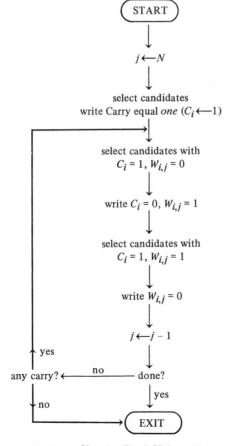

Fig. 5.24 Add one algorithm. (See also Fig. 5.25 for a slightly faster method.)

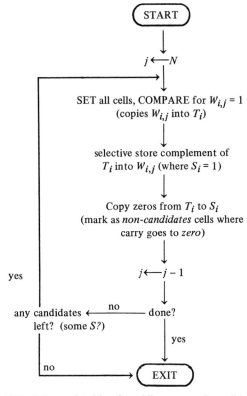

Fig. 5.25 A faster algorithm for adding one to all candidates.

and 5.26, we can simplify the algorithm as shown in Fig. 5.25. Candidates are originally marked with $S_i = 1$. As carry goes to *zero*, we no longer care about the cells so we mark them as being non-candidates (copy *zeros* T to S). This requires $4N$ steps.

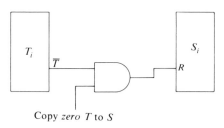

Copy *zero* T to S

Fig. 5.26 Special circuits needed for the algorithm of Fig. 5.25.

Add Fields

For the sake of being explicit, we will add the number stored in bits 1–10 to the number stored in bits 21–30, leaving the result in bits 21–30. We need one flag X to mark candidates and one to store the carry for each word.

Table 5.1 shows the initial conditions and the final conditions for adding A to B and putting the result in B. C is the carry bit.

TABLE 5.1   THE 8 POSSIBLE CONDITIONS FOR ADD FIELDS

Line	Old C B A	New C B	Comment
0	0 0 0	0 0	no action required
1	0 0 1	0 1	do after line 3
2	0 1 0	0 1	no action required
3	0 1 1	1 0	do before line 1
4	1 0 0	0 1	do before line 6
5	1 0 1	1 0	no action required
6	1 1 0	1 0	do after line 4
7	1 1 1	1 1	no action required

For lines 0, 2, 5, and 7, no action is required because the "old state" of B and C are identical with the new state. Line 1 converts the pattern 00 to 01 but line 3 changes 01 to 10. Therefore, we must do line 3 before line 1. Similarly, line 4 must preced line 6. Figure 5.27 shows the algorithm. To carry out the processing for line 3 takes five reads (SET, COMPARE $X = 1$, COMPARE $W_{i,j} = 1$, COMPARE $W_{i,j+20} = 1$, COMPARE $C_i = 0$) and two writes, or seven probes. Line 1 needs six probes, line 4 needs seven, and line 6 needs six. A grand total of $26N$ probes to perform "add fields." With multi-bit WRITE and COMPARE, this reduces to $12N$.

Aside from keeping the candidates marked in the selector bits of the response store, no particular advantage is to be gained from the more complicated circuits of this chapter until one puts in quite sophisticated hardware. In Chapter 6 we will see how STARAN performs the add fields algorithm. We propose the hardware of Fig. 5.28. We have hooked up R and T as a binary counter using the input "t" to trigger or complement the contents of a flip-flop.

We begin with the carry in R, (initially zero, of course) and T cleared to *zero*. We read $W_{i,j}$ to complement R_i. If R_i goes from the

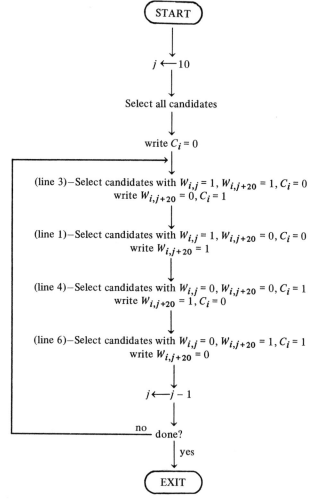

Fig. 5.27 Algorithm to add fields. The number stored in bits 1–10 is added to the number stored in bits 21–30.

one to the *zero* state $\overline{R}_i$ goes to *one* and T_i is set to *one*. Then we read $W_{i,j+20}$, again complementing R_i. This forms the sum in R_i and the carry in T_i. Details are shown in Fig. 5.29. Timing requires two reads and a write plus a transfer and a clear within the response store. That counts up to five probes per bit or $5N$ probes.

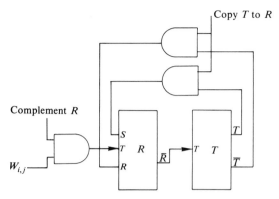

Fig. 5.28 Special hardware circuits for the add fields algorithm.

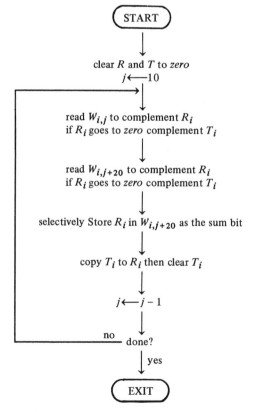

Fig. 5.29 The algorithm to use the special hardware of Fig. 5.28.

Add Constant

This algorithm will add a constant stored in the comparand register to every cell holding a candidate. For the machine of Chapter 2, we need one bit to flag candidates and one bit to hold the carry. The algorithm is an obvious variation of the algorithm to add fields and needs no further discussion. (See Fig. 5.30.)

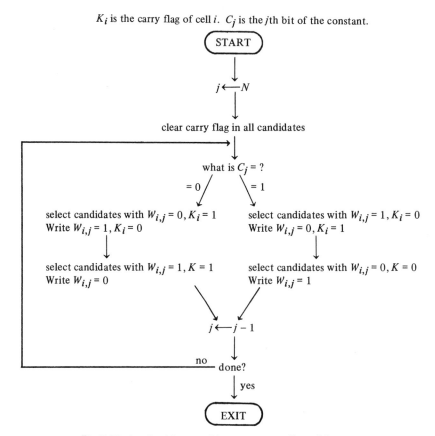

Fig. 5.30 An algorithm to add a constant to all candidates.

Question 5.10: Time this algorithm.

Similarly, the hardware for adding a constant is identical to hardware for adding fields using the complement R input when the bit of

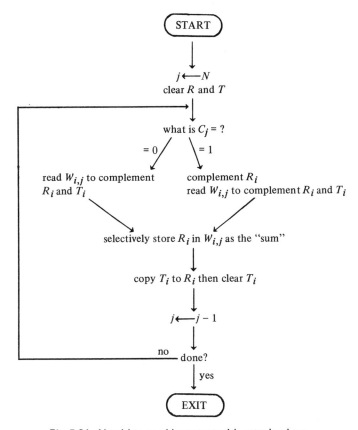

Fig. 5.31 Algorithm to add constant with extra hardware.

the constant is *one* and not using it if the bit is *zero*. The algorithm is shown in Fig. 5.31.

Question 5.11: Time this algorithm assuming zeros and ones are equally likely in the constant.

Subtract One

Perhaps the easiest way to subtract one from the candidate cells would be to add minus one. That would be the easiest way for the lazy author and lazy reader, but it would be too long. We can design a much faster algorithm analogous to the add one algorithm discussed above.

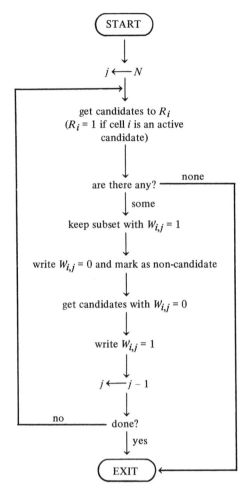

Fig. 5.32 An algorithm to subtract one from all candidates.

This algorithm is shown in Fig. 5.32. We use the fact that a cell is still an active candidate to indicate that the "borrow" has not yet been absorbed. In cells with borrow and $W_{i,j} = 1$, we write $W_{i,j} = 0$ and mark them as non-candidates. (Their borrow is taken care of.) In candidates with $W_{i,j} = 0$, we write $W_{i,j} = 1$ and leave them as candidates.

This algorithm requires $11N + 3$ probes to complete. Figures 5.33 and 5.34 show the special hardware and the algorithm for subtract one. Here again, we mark candidates with $S = 1$ and take

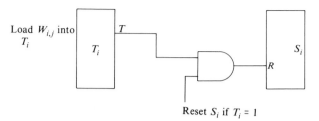

Fig. 5.33 Special hardware for subtract-one algorithm.

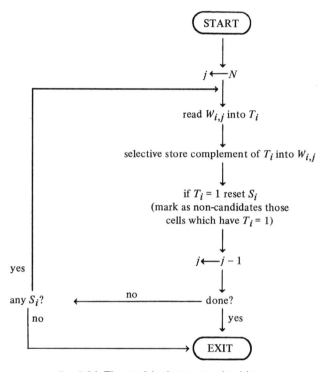

Fig. 5.34 The special subtract-one algorithm.

advantage of the store $\overline{R}$ function. This requires $3N$ memory references: a read, a write, and a reset S.

Subtract Fields

The same reasoning is applicable to the subtract fields algorithm as was applied to the add fields. We will subtract B and A and put the result in A. Using D as the deficit, or borrow, bit we have

Line Number	Initial	Final	
Number	D A B	D A B	
0	0 0 0	0 0 0	no change
1	0 0 1	1 1 1	
2	0 1 0	0 1 0	no change
3	0 1 1	0 0 1	
4	1 0 0	1 1 0	
5	1 0 1	1 0 1	no change
6	1 1 0	0 0 0	
7	1 1 1	1 1 1	no change

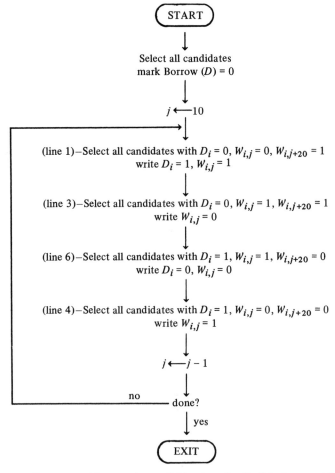

Fig. 5.35 An algorithm to subtract fields. $A \leftarrow A - B$. D is the carry bit.

Lines 0, 2, 5, and 7 require no action. Figure 5.35 shows the algorithm. Once again, we let A be bits 1–10 and B be bits 21–30. This algorithm takes $26N$ probes going one bit at a time and $12N$ for multi-bit WRITE and COMPARE.

Question 5.12: Does the order of processing lines matter?

To subtract fields in hardware, we use the circuit of Fig. 5.36. We copy the carry (borrow) from T_i to R_i, and $W_{i,j}$ and subtract $W_{i,j+20}$. Then we store responders into $W_{i,j}$ and repeat for the next bit.

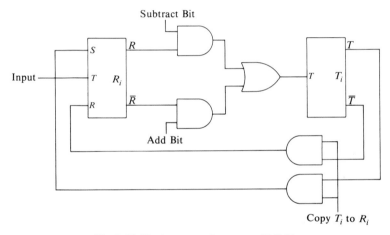

Fig. 5.36 Hardware to subtract or add fields.

Question 5.13: Diagram this algorithm.

Multiplication by a Constant

The standard scheme for multiplication in conventional von Neumann machines is called "add and shift." This is an admirable description of the technique. Let us consider it in some detail. It grows directly out of the old-fashioned hand method. Consider the following case:

$$
\begin{array}{r}
1101 \\
\times\ 1010 \\
\hline
0000 \\
1101 \\
0000 \\
1101 \\
\hline
10000010
\end{array}
\quad
\begin{array}{l}
\text{multiplicand} \\
\text{multiplier} \\
\\
\\
\\
\\
\\
\text{product}
\end{array}
$$

or 13 X 10 = 130 (128 + 2). Where the multiplier has *zeros* we add in *zeros*—a place keeping operation and not actually performed in a computer—and where the multiplier has *ones* we add in the multiplicand. As shown in Fig. 5.37, the multiplier and the partial product (initially zero) are stored in one double length register while the

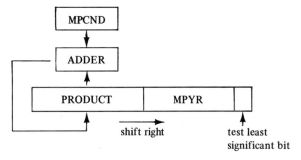

Fig. 5.37 Typical operation of the multiply instruction in a conventional digital computer.

multiplicand is stored in an ordinary register. The low order bit of the multiplier is tested. If it is a *zero*, the long register is shifted right one bit. If it is a *one*, the multiplicand is added in to the partial product and then the long register is shifted right one bit. After N shifts there is no more multiplier left, and the final product is left in the double length register. This scheme works least significant bit first and requires $N/2$ adds if half the multiplier bits are *zero*, and N shifts.

We will use a variation of this scheme for our CAPP, except that we will begin with the most significant bit of the multiplier instead of the least and we will do no bit shifting (Davis, 1963). A snapshot of the process is shown in Fig. 5.38 and Fig. 5.39 shows the algorithm.

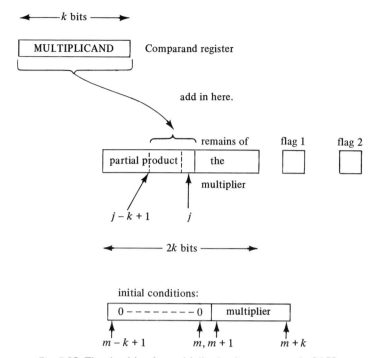

Fig. 5.38 The algorithm for multiplication by a constant in CAPP.

The initial conditions show a partial product of all *zeros* in bits $m - k + 1$ through m and the multiplier in bits $m + 1$ through $m + k$. The index i is set equal to $m + 1$ and addition, when it takes place, is done into bits $j - k + 1$ through j. If the $i - m^{\text{th}}$ bit of the multiplier is one, we set Flag 1 and add in the multiplicand to the partial product in bits j (the rightmost), through $j - k + 1$ (the leftmost) doing our addition right to left as usual and using Flag 2 as the carry bit. If the fields to be multiplied are k bits long, and if we use the add constant algorithm of Fig. 5.33, we will require the order of k^2 memory references.

Division

Just as multiplication is done by addition, division is usually done by subtraction. Suppose we wish to divide 11 by 3. The result should be 3 with a remainder of 2. In binary we have:

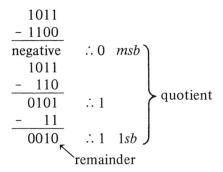

$$
\begin{array}{ll}
1011 & \\
-\ 1100 & \\
\hline
\text{negative} & \therefore 0 \quad msb \\
1011 & \\
-\ \ \ 110 & \\
\hline
0101 & \therefore 1 \\
-\ \ \ \ 11 & \\
\hline
0010 & \therefore 1 \quad lsb \\
\end{array}
$$

quotient

remainder

We present in Fig. 5.40 an algorithm that divides field X of every word by a constant and places the quotient in field Y and leaves the

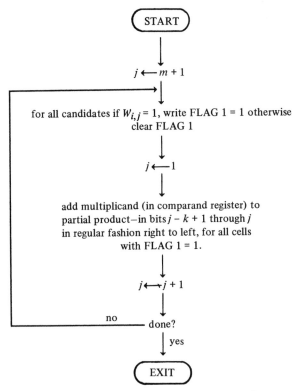

Fig. 5.39 The multiply algorithm. Flag 1 is set to *one* if the $j - m^{\text{th}}$ bit of the multiplier is a *one*. Flag 2 is used as the carry bit for addition.

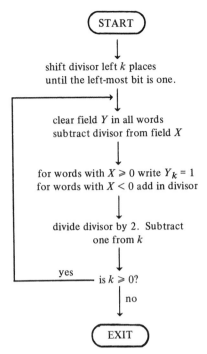

START

shift divisor left k places
until the left-most bit is one.

clear field Y in all words
subtract divisor from field X

for words with $X \geqslant 0$ write $Y_k = 1$
for words with $X < 0$ add in divisor

divide divisor by 2. Subtract
one from k

yes

is $k \geqslant 0$?

no

EXIT

Fig. 5.40 Divide by constant.

remainder in X. Once again, we confine ourselves to positive numbers.

Normalize Floating Point Numbers

After performing a floating point operation, it is conventional to "normalize" the result; that is, to shift left until the sign bit and the most significant bit of the word differ, subtracting one from the exponent for each left shift. Since we are going to shift into the most significant bit (b) over-writing it anyway, we can use b to hold the borrow during the subtract. (See Fig. 5.41.)

Minimum Hamming Distance

Quite often when we fail to find an exact match to a comparand, we would like to find the "best" match. If we define "best" to mean differing in the fewest number of places, this becomes a search for the *Minimum Hamming Distance*. If this is an attempt to match a

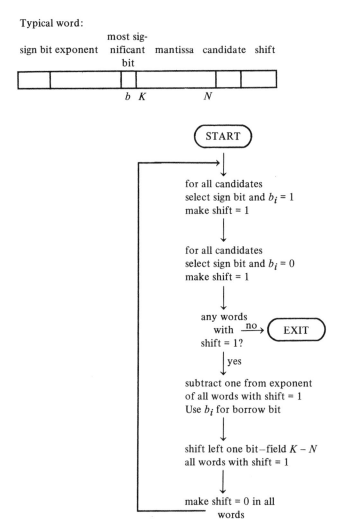

Fig. 5.41 Normalize floating point numbers.

noisy signal with a group of stored patterns, and if we have selected the patterns so that the Minimum Hamming Distance between any pair of patterns is two, we have a single error correction code. If $H = 3$ we have single error correction and double error detection. Figure 5.42 shows an algorithm for finding the "closest" match under this definition.

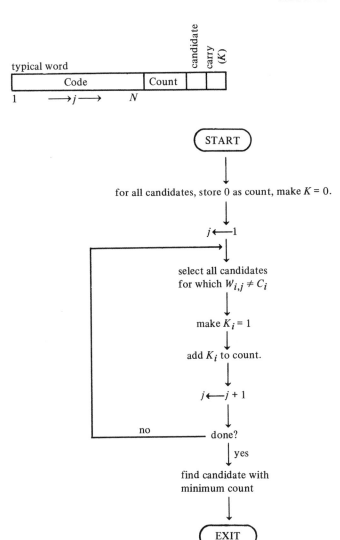

Fig. 5.42 An algorithm for finding the "closest" match.

We select those candidates that differ from the comparand in the ith position and add one to their count of differences. When we have treated all bits, we find the candidate with the minimum number of differences. That is then, by definition, the closest match.

OTHER ALGORITHMS

We will close this chapter with three algorithms which utilize the "count responders" feature sometimes included in CAPP's; for example, machine 3 of Chapter 2. These algorithms will find the mean, the median, and the mode of an array of elements. Aside from the fact that they are all standard statistical operations, they each exemplify a different method of using the hardware.

The Mean

In order to find the mean value of an assemblage of elements, we add them all up and then divide by the number of elements. We will assume for simplicity that either the sum is small enough to fit into a central register, or, what comes to the same thing, that the register is long enough to hold the sum. Consider an array of three words, each four bits long, as shown below:

$$1\ 1\ 0\ 0 = 12$$
$$1\ 1\ 1\ 0 = 14$$
$$0\ 1\ 0\ 0 = 4$$

and assume we wish to find the sum. Our algorithm is expressed by the equation:

$$\{[((2 * 2) + 3) * 2] + 1\}\ 2 + 0 = 30$$

The leftmost column has two *ones* in it. We double this number and add to it the number of *ones* (3) in the second column. We double this, add in the number of *ones* in the third column (1); double this partial sum and add to it the number of *ones* (0) in the last column. The result is 30 and is indeed the sum of 12, 14, and 4. The general algorithm is shown in Fig. 5.43. For each bit position, this algorithm takes three probes to set and get all the candidates with $W_{i,j} = 1$. This requires the order of $3N$ probes. If it takes A probe times to let the adder circuits stabilize, we need a total of $(3 + A)N$ probe times. Of course, if $A = 0$, this reduces to $3N + 2$.

Figure 5.44 shows a circuit to perform this algorithm in $(1 + A) \cdot (N + 1)$ probe times.

Question 5.14: Diagram this algorithm.

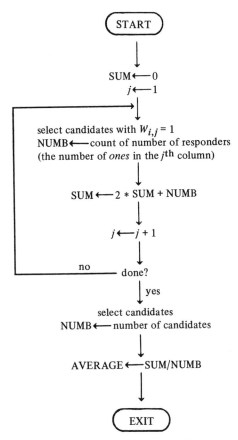

Fig. 5.43 An algorithm to find the mean value of an array of elements.

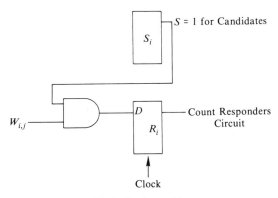

Fig. 5.44 A circuit to add an array.

The Median

The median of an array is defined to be that value such that half the elements are greater than the value and the remaining half is less than the value. Suppose it is known that the elements of the array are restricted to values lying between $\pm X$, and further, that there are Y candidates. If these facts are unknown, they can be quickly ascertained.

We make an initial guess at the value (V) of the median. We will guess 0 as lying halfway between the extremes. We then select all candidates greater than V and count them. If the number of such candidates (K) is greater than $Y/2$, we have guessed too low a value for V. So we try a larger value at, say, $X/2$. Now we find the number of candidates greater than V to be less than $Y/2$ so we try a value of V halfway between the present value and the last one or $X/4$. We continue until we get K exactly equal to $Y/2$. Figure 5.45 shows the algorithm. DELTA is the step size that we add or subtract from V to get the new value of V. It is initially set to $X/2$.

This is the same technique as is used to perform a binary search of a table and requires $\log_2 X$ steps. Each step of course requires several probes of memory to select the candidates greater than V.

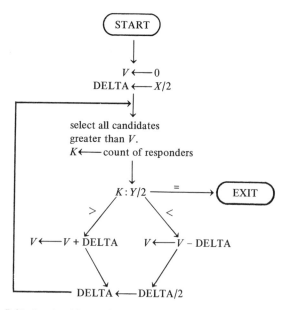

Fig. 5.45 An algorithm to find the median of an array of Y elements.

The Mode

In statistics, the mode is defined to be the value that occurs most often. Our approach is to take the first candidate, count how many elements are equal to it, and then mark them "processed." Then we take the next candidate in order of occurrence, not necessarily in order of size, and count the number of elements equal to that. We keep the larger of the two counts (and the value associated with it) as a "trial mode." We continue selecting and counting, keeping always the more popular value as the trial mode until all different values have been exhausted. Figure 5.46 shows the algorithm which, if all elements are different, takes Y steps.

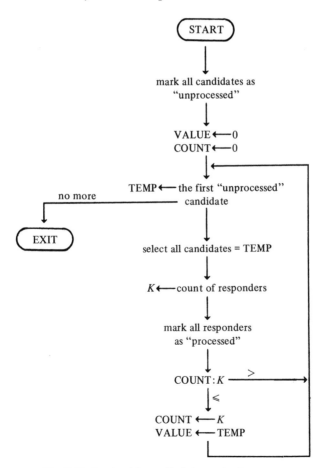

Fig. 5.46 An algorithm to find the mode of an array.

These three algorithms are respectively independent of the number of elements, dependent on the log of the number and dependent on the number of elements. A conventional computer would take the order of Y steps to compute the mean by successive additions, $Y \cdot \log_2 Y$ steps to get the median and Y^2 to compute the mode.*

SUMMARY

In this chapter we have looked in great detail at a number of algorithms for CAPP's. The casual reader will have skipped most of this detail and the earnest one may perhaps be a bit overwhelmed by it. There are reasons for having presented this amount of detail. First of all, there are the skeptics to quiet. Second, some one might someday actually build a CAPP and use this chapter for reference. Finally, we need timing estimates so we can know how fast or how slow CAPP's are at parallel operations.

Now it has been done. It can be absorbed into the hardware or firmware of all CAPP's, actual or hypothetical, and the ultimate user of CAPP's will know no more about the details of these algorithms than he does now about how the FORTRAN sine routine works.

*The mode can be computed by pigeon hole sorting if the range is small enough. We ignore this in the above.

6 | APPLICATIONS OF CAPP'S

In this chapter we will investigate a few applications of Content Addressable Parallel Processors. We have attempted to find a number of different problems and apply the CAPP to them. It is important to convince the reader that the range of application is large; far larger than the rather limited class of problems that an array processor can handle. It has been said that ILLIAC IV and its array-type brethren are good only for "relaxation nets," and CAPP's are good only for "radar data processing," whatever that may be. It is to be hoped that by the time you have finished this chapter you will recognize that at least the last half of the previous sentence is obviously wrong.

We have not selected the following applications scientifically. We selected them over a period of several years as being interesting and as displaying some of the capabilities of a CAPP type of organization. Treatment will be of varying depth depending on my insight, interest, and available energy. The references at the end of this chapter include other applications that the reader might want to examine.

RADAR ANALYZER

Suppose we are sitting in the middle of a battlefield and on every side of us there are radar sets, some friendly and some hostile. It would be to our advantage if we could sort out the pulses that impinge upon us and say, "There is a transmitter with such and such characteristics located on thus and so bearing, and another one on this bearing and still another on that." Let us try to design a system that will do this. We suppose that we have a pair of omnidirectional receivers to collect all the pulses coming our way, and measure the difference in arrival time between the two receivers to give an indication of bearing. We will try first to do this with a conventional computer.

Typical radar sets have constant amplitude pulses and a fixed interpulse interval. Pulse repetition frequencies (PRF'S) vary between 50 and 200 pulses per second, giving pulse intervals in the range of 5 to 20 milliseconds. If we keep the history of all pulses that have arrived for the last 60 milliseconds, we will have at least four pulses from even the lowest PRF radar. We will store the time of arrival of each pulse and its bearing (as indicated by the difference in time between the two receivers.) Let the most recent pulse be called P_0, the one before that P_1, and so forth.

When a new pulse arrives, we note the time. The age of each pulse in our history is given by $A_i = T_0 - T_i$. We pick up pulse P_1 with age A_1 and then look for a string of pulses with ages $2A, 3A, \ldots,$. If we find such a string, and if the bearings are reasonably consistent, we say we have found a source at bearing B_1 with PRF $= 1/A_1$. We then look at pulse P_2 with age A_2 and see if we can establish a source with bearing B_2 and PRF $= 1/A_2$. We continue doing this until we get to some pulse P_i for which $1/A_i$ is smaller than the smallest PRF of interest.

Suppose we are receiving 5000 pulses per second. With a mean PRF of 100, that represents about 50 transmitters; which makes for a reasonably crowded battlefield. It also implies that we are getting a new pulse every 200 μsec, so we had best be done analyzing in that time period; assuming that we want to do this processing in real time and not drop ever farther behind. If we try to establish sequences for all pulses in our history with ages between 5 and 20 milliseconds (called defining pulses), we will have five pulses per millisecond times 15 milliseconds, or 75 pulse trains to search for, or only 2 to 3 μsec per train for searching. Further, if we say that four pulses are necessary to establish a train, then having the new pulse P_0 and the "defining pulse" with its age A_i, we must look for a pulse with age $2A_i$ and one with age $3A_i$. This gives us around 1 μsec for each search.

Since pulses are arriving in order of age in a conventional computer, we could do a binary search to see if a pulse of appropriate age and bearing exists. Keeping a 60 millisecond history of 5 pulses per millisecond implies 300 pulses in the history. Linear search of 300 items in 1.5 μsec would of course be completely out of the question. A binary search would take $\log_2$ 300 or about eight or nine probes to determine if an item is present or not. A one μsecond memory cycle RAM would be about ten times too slow. Given that we know about where to start looking since we know the desired age, we might do a little better than this.

Consider now the solution of the problem using a CAM. We will suppose that we keep the history in both a conventional memory (RAM) and in a CAM, and that these two memories can be interrogated independently. We get the next "defining pulse" from the RAM and with high speed circuitry determine its age A_i. We compute the time at which pulses P_j and P_k would have had to arrive: $T_0 - 2A_i$ and $T_0 - 3A_i$ and in two probes of a one μsec bit parallel search memory we know whether or not such a train of pulses exists. We can have fetched the next defining pulse from the RAM while we were doing this.

We can now further complicate the problem a little by assuming that there is some uncertainty (jitter) in the time of arrival of a pulse. Let that uncertainty be Δt and assume we are keeping time in units of Δt. Then in looking for a pulse that should have arrived at t_i, we must also look at $t_i + \Delta t$ and $t_i - \Delta t$. This adds two more probes in a RAM for each t_i sought, but in a CAM it adds only one, because we can take advantage of the ability to mask out the low order bit of the desired comparand (t_i). This automatically searches for t_i and either $t_i + \Delta t$ or $t_i - \Delta t$ depending on whether t_i was even or odd, respectively. We then follow this with an unmasked search for the remaining condition. This requires only two probes. In summary, then, a one μsec CAM/RAM combination is just fast enough, a linearly searched one μsec RAM is 300 times too slow, and a binary searched one μsec RAM is about ten times too slow.

TESTS OF CONNECTIVITY

In a large number of applications, we desire to find out if point A is connected to point B either directly or through a chain of intermediaries (Levitt, 1972 and Crane, 1968). Finding a path in a digraph or determining implications in an artificial intelligence seman-

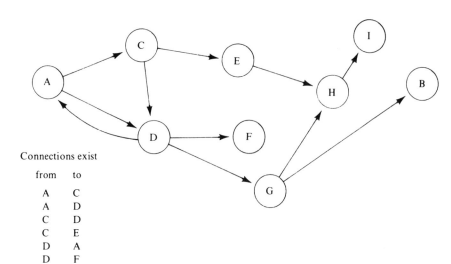

Connections exist

from	to
A	C
A	D
C	D
C	E
D	A
D	F
D	G
E	H
G	H
G	B
H	I

Fig. 6.1 A typical small digraph.

tic net are only two examples of such searches: Fig. 6.1 shows a typical small digraph and the lists of facts about the graph that must be stored in a computer's memory. In "depth first" searches, we go to a child of a node before we explore other siblings of that node. In "breadth first" exactly the reverse is true. In depth first searching, we would find the path A-C-D before we found A-D.

Thus, in a depth-first search we would visit nodes A-C-E-H-I-H-E-C-D-F-D-G-B while in a breadth-first we would activate

A

C D

ED*FGA*

HHB

where the * indicates that the node has already been visited.

In the CAPP we are going to do a breadth-first search leaving a trail behind so that we can retrace our path from the terminal node back to the initial node. We will store information in the CAPP one connection per cell with four fields: source, destination, counter, flag. One such cell will exist for each connection of the graph. Initially all counters and flags will be set to *zero*. We take the starting node (A) and select all cells that have that node as a source and mark their counters with a *one*. We test to see if any cell with count of 1 has B (the target node) as a destination. We then select the first cell with counter of *one* and flag of *zero,* mark the flag as *one* to indicate it has been processed, and read out its destination. Using that destination as a source, we select all cells with that source and counter of *zero* and write 2 in their counters. We repeat for all cells with counter of *one.* This gives the following memory picture for the digraph of Fig. 6.1:

$$A, C, 1, 1 \qquad C, D, 2, 0$$
$$A, D, 1, 1 \qquad C, E, 2, 0$$
$$D, A, 2, 0$$
$$D, F, 2, 0$$
$$D, G, 2, 0$$

First we test to see if any second generation cell (Count = 2) has B as a destination. If so, we are through; otherwise, we select, in turn, cells with counters of 2 and flags of 0 and mark their descendents (with initial counter of *zero*) with a count of 3. The first cell of the second generation has D as a destination, but since D has already been visited (the flag is set in all cells leading away from D), no new activity is generated. When we have activated all the new descendents of the second generation, we go on to the third, then the fourth. Figure 6.2 displays the algorithm.

To complete the tracing of the net we have

$$E, H, 3, 0$$
$$G, B, 3, 0$$
$$G, H, 3, 0$$

after processing all cells of the second generation. Since B is among the destinations we have reached our goal and we know that a path does exist, and as a matter of fact, we have found the shortest path. Now the problem remaining is to read the path out of memory.

To find the pathway, we begin at the end and work backward. B is the ultimate destination, so we look for a cell with B as destination and with a count of non zero. We find the cell with G, B, 3. So the link G-B is part of the path. Next, we look for a cell with G as a destination and a count one less than what we had the previous

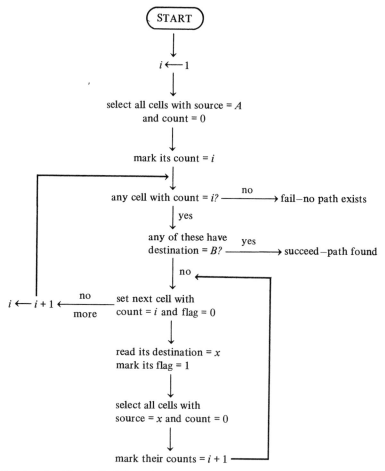

Fig. 6.2 An algorithm to find if a path exists between *A* and *B*. Initially all counts and flags are zero.

time, namely: 2. The cell containing D, G, 2 is found. Now we look for a cell with ?, D, 1. That cell is A, D, 1 and we are back to the starting node. So the path is A-D-G-B.

Suppose instead that H had been the terminal node. When we ask for links impinging on H we find E, H, 3 and also G, H, 3. Since we are looking for the shortest path we will naturally choose the link of the youngest generation (the one with the smallest count field.) If, as in this case, two or more links have equal age, we choose one among them arbitrarily. A flow diagram for this process is shown in Fig. 6.3.

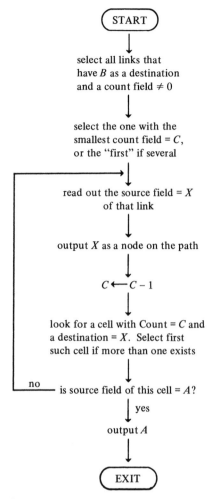

Fig. 6.3 An algorithm for selecting the shortest path between *A* and *B* in a net that was "numbered" by the algorithm of Fig. 6.2.

The algorithm for numbering the links (See Fig. 6.2) is probably not a great deal faster than what would run in a conventional machine, because all the cells of a generation must be treated sequentially. We do mark all the "out links" of a given node in parallel and that might represent a speed-up of a factor of two or three depending how may "outlinks" an average node has. Where we really gain is in the algorithm to read out the path. First off we take advantage of the fact that, by storing the links in a CAPP we have implicitly stored the back links. [Note that in our representation there is no place one can point to and say that it represents the node. What we are storing is the links.]

Without building some kind of complicated tree structure while numbering the net, or without cumbersome searches, it is hard to see how the algorithm of Fig. 9.3 could be employed in a conventional machine.

It might be interesting to consider this digraph problem in a tessellated CAPP arranged in a square grid. We leave that as an exercise for the reader.

SPELLING CORRECTOR

Consider a word as received over a Teletype line. Frequently it is garbled in transmission or in the original typing, for Teletype operators are not necessarily the best typists or spellers in the world.

The most common types of error are

> —wrong letter
> —dropped letter
> —added letter
> —interchanged letter pair

Let us attempt to design a system that will correct single errors (Goodyear, 1965c). We will store a dictionary and when a word arrives over the line we will look it up in the dictionary. If we find it we assume that that was what was intended. It might be an error that converted one legitimate word into another. English is prone to such errors, not being a Hamming code. If we fail to find the received word, we will try to see if any of the four types of errors listed above could have converted a legitimate dictionary word into what we have received. If only one such transformation exists, we will say that we have succeeded in correcting the word. If more than one exists, we will admit our confusion and go on to the next word.

As an example, consider the received word

P E R A

which we do not find in the dictionary. To test for possible wrong letters we institute searches for

```
?  E  R  A
P  ?  R  A
P  E  ?  A
P  E  R  ?
```

and discover that PERT is a possible reconstruction. Next we assume that what we received was what was left after a letter got dropped. So we look for:

```
?  P  E  R  A
P  ?  E  R  A
P  E  ?  R  A
P  E  R  ?  A
P  E  R  A  ?
```

and find OPERA. To see if an extra letter got stuck in by mistake we eliminate each in turn and search for:

```
E  R  A
P  R  A
P  E  A
P  E  R
```

Of these, all but P R A are English words, so we now have five possible reconstructions. Finally, we test for transposed letter pairs and get:

```
E  P  R  A
P  R  E  A
P  E  A  R
```

of which the last is clearly a word.

Brief consideration shows that for an N letter word there is one search for correct spelling, there are N individual letters that might be wrong, $N + 1$ places to add back a letter, N possible letters to discard, and $N - 1$ adjacent pairs to interchange. This comes to a total of $4N + 1$ searches to perform.

The most obvious way to approach this problem is to store the dictionaries in a CAPP and do the $4N + 1$ searches when a word comes along. The average word in English is five characters, so this implies 20 additional searches if the first search shows an error has been received. In a one μsec parallel by bit search CAPP it would take 20 μsec to do these 20 searches. If we could do a serial by *byte* search looking at a whole character of eight bits at a time we would take 100 μsec and if only serial by bit searches are available, we would need eight times that much, or 800 μsec. Assuming 100 ns serial by bit memories would still require 80 μsec.

It is possible to reduce the number of searches substantially if the dictionary is small enough or the CAM large enough. Let us define a "reduction" of a word as being that word with one of its letters removed and the resulting space closed up. An N letter word then has N reductions plus the original word. If the average word is five letters long, this requires $N + 1$ or six times as much space. We store a reduction in the left half of a cell and the original form in the right half. Now one search will test whether the received word is present *and* whether the received word is a longer word with a character dropped.

Further, let us add up modulo 256 the ASCII representations of the letters of the received word calling this the hash sum of the word. If we store the hash sum of each of the words in the dictionary, we can tell in one search whether a pairwise transposition has occurred. Of course, we will get some false positives, since the sum is not unique but in the case of no match to the hash sum we perform only one search instead of $N - 1$.

If now we define the "expansion" of a dictionary word to be that word padded with an extra blank character we have $N + 1$ expansions of an N letter word and we can search for "wrong letter" and "extra letter" at the same time requiring N searches.

In total then, we would have one search for correct-or-dropped-letter, one search for hash sum for transposed letters and N searches for wrong-or-added-letter, or a total of $N + 2$ searches. We have, in exchange, increased the size of our dictionary by 13 times, assuming average five letter words; a classical tradeoff of space versus time.

If this represents too much expansion in the size of the dictionary, we can compromise and keep the dictionary unexpanded and do the searches in $3N - 2$ character comparisons as follows. We construct a response store with four bits called A, D, T, W (add, drop, transpose, wrong.) We break the cells of memory and the comparand into bytes of one character each. We are going to compare each character (C_i) of the comparand with three characters of each memory word (W_{i-1}, W_i, and W_{i+1}) (see Fig. 6.4). These are called respectively, γ,

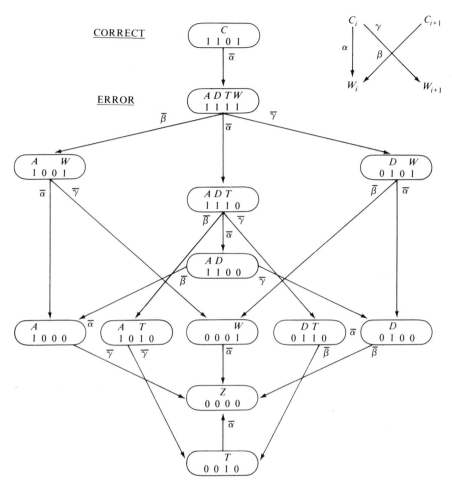

Fig. 6.4 State transition diagram for Spelling Correction hardware when searches are done serially.

α, and β type comparisons and if a word and the comparand disagree on a particular search (say $C_5 : W_4$) we designate this with a $\overline{\gamma}$ in this case.

The pattern of searches is

$$
\begin{aligned}
&\text{compare } C_i && \text{with } W_i, && \alpha_i \\
&\text{compare } C_i && \text{with } W_{i+1}, && \beta_i \\
&\text{compare } C_{i+1} && \text{with } W_i, && \gamma_i
\end{aligned}
$$

and then go on to the next character.

Figure 6.4 shows the state transition diagram for this response store. This diagram is more understandable if we break it down into parts.

First of all, we start each cell in the "correct" state which can be represented by any arbitrary assignment of $ADTW$ not used elsewhere in the diagram. We have chosen 1101. Now, as long as the word and the comparand compare character for character we stay in the "correct" state, but as soon as a character is detected that does not compare (generates an $\bar{\alpha}$) that word is transferred to a state called "Error." This state is represented by $ADTW = 1111$ since at this point any type of error is possible. Consider first the *added letter case*:

$$\text{Comparand:} \quad A \;\; B \;\; X \;\; C \;\; D \;\; E$$
$$\gamma \;\; \gamma \;\; \gamma$$
$$\text{Word } K: \quad A \;\; B \;\; C \;\; D \;\; E$$

We find on the third α test that X and C are not equal so we move to the Error State. From now on, if this is to be an added letter case, we must insist that all γ type comparisons are successful. As soon as we get a $\bar{\gamma}$ we can reset (clear) the A flip-flop because we know that it wasn't an added letter case. If we end up with A still set, we can conclude that the reverse is true. Examination of Fig. 6.4 shows that from every state that has $A = 1$ (except "correct") a $\bar{\gamma}$ will reset A. The circuitry for this is shown in Fig. 6.5.

The case of a dropped letter is similar except that we see that once we have left the correct state, any "forward mismatch" $(\bar{\beta})$ will preclude the case and hence reset the D flip-flop. Fig. 6.4 and 6.5 confirm this.

The case of transposed letters looks like:

$$\text{Comparand:} \quad A \;\; B \quad\quad D \;\; C \;\; E$$
$$\alpha_3$$
$$\text{Word } K: \quad A \;\; B \quad\quad C \;\; D \;\; E$$

Again, failure of α_3 converts word k to the error state. In the error state the next forward match (β_3) and the next backward match (γ_3) must both succeed for this to be a transposed letter case. Therefore, E (error state) and either $\bar{\beta}$ or $\bar{\gamma}$ cause T to reset. Note that the error state is the only one where both T and W are set. Now observe that

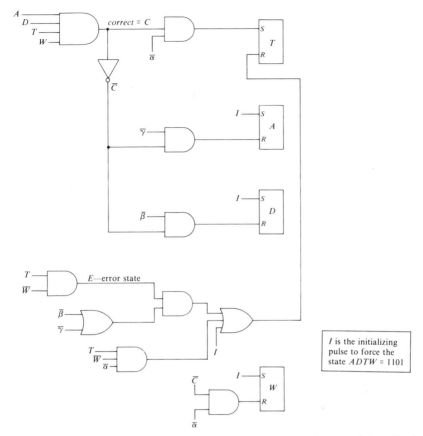

Fig. 6.5 Response Store Circuitry for the fast spelling corrector where searches are in the order of α, β, then γ.

if α_i failed and β_i and γ_i succeeded, then α_{i+1} must fail as well. As we shall see, that failure removes us from the error state and any further failure of α indicates that an additional error has been detected and we cannot be in the simple transposed letter condition. Thus, in any state except correct, error, or ZERO (that is when T is true and W is false) a detection of an $\overline{\alpha}$ will reset T.

Finally, looking for the wrong letter case we note that as soon as we are not in the correct state (as soon as we have detected an $\overline{\alpha}$) the occurrence of an $\overline{\alpha}$ (a second direct mismatch) means that at least two letters disagree and we cannot end up with W set.

Since we do not need to perform either β or γ for the last character, we have $3N - 2$ comparisons for N characters.

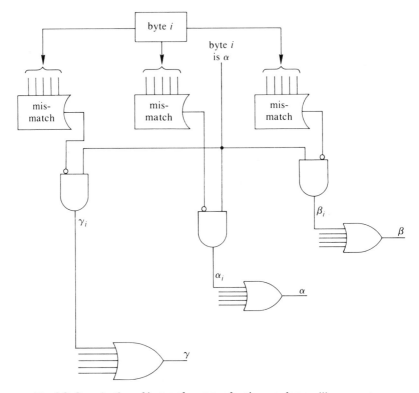

Fig. 6.6 Organization of bytes of memory for the very fast spelling corrector.

It is possible to gain even more speed if we arrange to do the α, β and γ searches in parallel. To keep the cell logic as simple as possible, we will simultaneously compare C_i with W_{i-1}, W_i, and W_{i+1} rather than put in three sets of comparison logic at each cell. At each byte in memory we have an additional line saying that "this byte is the α-byte at this time." This line also goes to the byte on the left saying it is the γ-byte and to the byte on the right saying it is the β-byte. This circuit for one triple of bytes is shown in Fig. 6.6.

Figure 6.7 shows the circuit required. Two additional flip-flops (C and T') were introduced to simplify the logic. The details are left to the reader.

DIGITAL DIFFERENTIAL ANALYZER

Analog computers, otherwise known as differential analyzers, suffer from high initial cost and low accuracy. Digital Differential

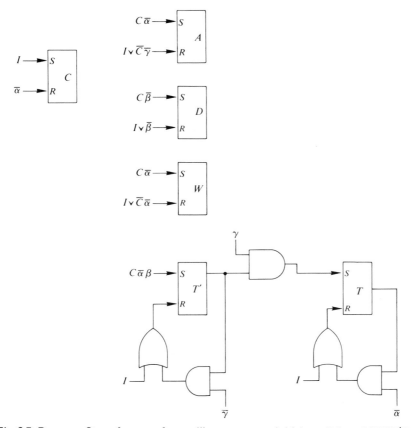

Fig. 6.7 Response Store for very fast spelling corrector. Initial conditions *CADWT'T* = 100 000.

Analyzers (DDA's) are an attempt to cure these problems while still retaining the ease of programming and flexibility of an analog device (Dawoud, 1973).   In this section we will design a DDA based on a CAPP that operates with moderate accuracy (twenty bits) and fair speed (nine μsec per amplifier per time step).

We are going to assume a CAPP with words 95 bits long with add/subtract hardware for each word in the response store. We will assume all operations are bit-serial at a rate of 100 nanoseconds per bit. Our memory will be 1000 words long, giving a DDA with 1000 amplifiers.

Basic operation of a DDA consists of the following steps:

1. For each amplifier, sum the inputs to that amplifier.

2. Scale the input by the gain factor G.
3. If this is a summing amplifier, *put* $- G \Sigma V_i$ into the output register.
4. If this is an integrating amplifier, *add* the scaled input to the output register.

Repeat for all amplifiers of the machine.

In a real analog computer the output of one amplifier is connected to the input of another via a patch cord so any amplifier may be connected to any other. In our DDA, each amplifier has a name (a ten bit number) and has the capability of receiving up to three inputs by storing the names of three other amplifiers in the fields IA, IB, and IC.

If more than three inputs are required, they can be concentrated three at a time in extra amplifiers. This will, of course, invert the subsidiary sums but that can be rectified by use of still another amplifier set up with one input and unity gain.

In our system, we will have possible gains of up to 32 in steps of 1/32 each. That is, we will use ten bits to hold the gain constant and assume a "decimal" point half way across the field.

The details of the several fields in each cell are shown in Fig. 6.8. The algorithm is shown in Fig. 6.9.

We get the next cell (A_i) that is in use (ON) and then we select all cells that have this cell's name (A_i) as one of their inputs (either IA,

size	use	
10	NAME	holds the name of this cell (1 – 1023)
10	IA	name of one amplifier inputing to this one
10	IB	name of second input
10	IC	name of third input
20	OUT	the output field of this amplifier
20	TEMP	a temporary field for computation
10	GAIN	the scale factor
1	INT	this amplifier is an integrator?
1	OVF	overflow occurred
1	ON	this amplifier in use
1	DONE	this amplifier has been processed
1	HERE	this amplifier is part of the set S.
95		

Fig. 6.8 Fields of each amplifier cell of the DDA.

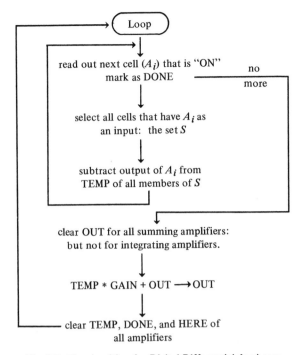

Fig. 6.9 The algorithm for Digital Differential Analyzer.

IB, or IC), and subtract the output of A_i from TEMP of these cells. This subtraction performs the inversion expected of an analog amplifier.

Assuming a 100 nanosecond bit serial memory, it takes 0.3 μsec to select and mark the next "undone" amplifier, one μsec to read its name and two μsec to get its output. It then takes an additional 3.3 μsec to select the amplifiers that have A_i as an input and 2 μsec to do the subtraction. This totals to 8.6 μsec per amplifier in use. If all 1000 amplifiers are in use, this requires 8.6 milliseconds. It then takes 2.1 μsec to clear the output register of summing amplifiers, and 20 μsec to compute the new value of the output. Finally, it requires 2.2 μsec to clear TEMP and the flags DONE and HERE to get ready for another loop.

Therefore, for N amplifiers in use, it takes $24.3 + 8.6N$ μsec for each update. By rough estimate, a conventional von Neuman machine would require three to five times as long.

LIST AND STRING PROCESSING

A number of list and string processing languages exist for conventional machines. Among these are IPL-V, LISP, SLIP, COMIT, and SNOBOL. Perhaps the single common salient feature of these languages is that they all attempt to allow the user to treat the storage of the computer as if it were elastic, rather than rigid. By this I mean that given an ordered set of items, A, B, C, D, it should be possible to insert a new item anywhere in the set (say A, B, X, D, E) or to delete an item from the set and close up the gap (say A, B, D). This is usually done either by time consuming moves of data or by space consuming pointers to the "next" item. This latter method is called a linked list. Each cell of storage is arranged to hold one item and one pointer. For example, the ordered set (list) A, B, C, D might be stored as shown in Fig. 6.10.

address	item	link
100	A	511
136	D	0
203	C	136
511	B	203

Fig. 6.10 A conventional linked list. A link of *zero* indicates the end of the list.

The major drawback of this organization becomes evident when we ask if item K is on the list. We must search every item on the list until we reach the end before we can decide that the item is not present. As lists become large, this becomes slow.

Figure 6.11 indicates a way in which a CAPP might be arranged to speed the searching of such lists. Each "ordered set" or list has a head cell which contains the number of entries on the list. Each data cell repeats the set name, contains an entry name, which serves to preserve the order of the items, and holds the item.

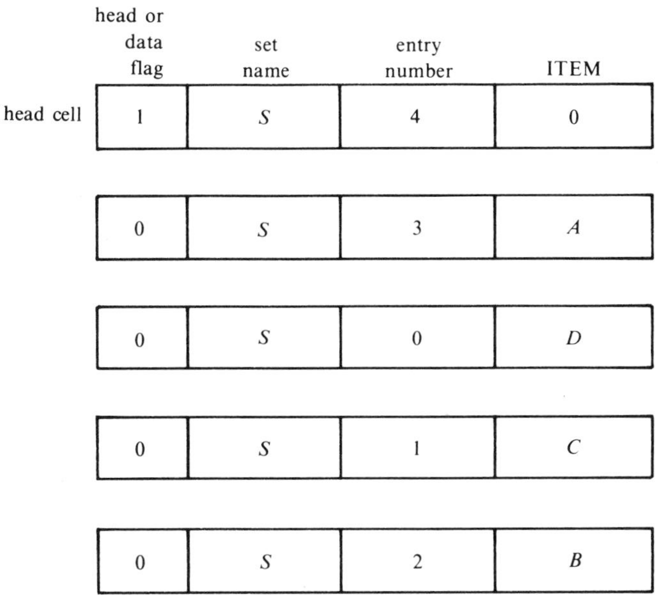

head or data flag	set name	entry number	ITEM

head cell

1	S	4	0

0	S	3	A

0	S	0	D

0	S	1	C

0	S	2	B

Fig. 6.11 An ordered set (S) stored in a CAPP.

To search the list for a specific item, we select all cells with the given set name and then do an exact match for the item. This is obviously fast and independent of the length of the list.

To insert a new item, say between items B and C, we perform a four step process:

1. find the cell containing item B.
2. Select all cells that are members of S and contain entry numbers greater than or equal to the entry number of B. (This will be the head cell, the cell containing A and the cell containing B).
3. Add one to the entry number of these cells.
4. Store the new item in a cell with the appropriate set name and with an entry number equal to the old entry number of B (in this case two.)

Deletion can be done in either of two ways. The first way is to just erase the entry. This is fast, but it leaves gaps in the sequence of entry numbers and when we wish to process a list sequentially, we must search for "the next smaller than" the previous number rather than an exact match search for $n - 1$. Further, with this scheme, the entry number in the head cell does not correspond to the number of items on the list. Since all fields are finite, this might cause us to run out of entry numbers earlier than necessary. Of course, it would be possible to institute a garbage collection—compression of gaps—routine when this happened, but that is an added complication it would be just as nice to do without.

The other scheme for deletion is the inverse of insertion:

1. Find the cell to be deleted and read its entry number E_i.
2. Erase the cell.
3. Select all members of the set with entry numbers greater than E_i.
4. Subtract one from the entry number of these cells.

This approach takes longer to do the deletion, but it avoids all the difficulties mentioned above and is probably to be preferred.

The next area in which CAPP's offer advantages for list processing is in the management of available space. Most list languages store unused cells on a linked list and remove a cell from the list when a one is needed elsewhere. When a list is erased, its cells are returned to the available space list, usually one by one. SLIP is noteworthy for being able to return a list intact to available space.

In a CAPP we handle the problem by storing all *zeros* in unused cells. Then an exact match search for set name of *zero* and a select-first-responder provides us with a new cell. To erase a single cell, we simply write *zero* into it and it returns automatically to the pool. To erase a whole list, we select all members of the list and write zeros into them in parallel.

Furthermore, should it be important, this scheme of handling available space keeps the used cells quite well packed toward one end of storage. Whenever new cells are needed, the "early" ones are used up first. This might have some advantage if it were desired to roll the user out of storage at any time. In general, those operations which are by their very nature sequential (find next item, for example) will not benefit substantially from a CAPP while those which involve searches will.

An example of a parallel search might be found in a typical SNOBOL pattern match. There we may ask for all the instances of the pattern "$ABC\emptyset D$" where the $\emptyset$ stands for one unspecified character intervening between the C and the D. To perform this efficiently, we need the "move activity forward" operation discussed previously, via which cells can transfer their "responderhood" to the cells immediately following them in the memory. We arrange to store one symbol (letter) per cell. Operation is as follows:

1. Activate all cells containing the symbol A.
2. Move activity forward one cell.
3. Reset (discard) any active cells that do not hold a symbol B.
4. Move activity forward one cell.
5. Discard any cell that does not contain a symbol C.

At this point we have all the occurrences of the pattern ABC marked as active in their C cell.

6. Move activity forward two cells.
7. If this cell holds a "D" mark it.

At the completion of step 7, all occurrences of ABC∅D have been marked and any desired changes can then be made. If these changes involve straight replacement, say of the "C" by an "X", they can be done in parallel. If, on the other hand, more complicated operations are desired, such as inserting a character between the "B" and the "C", it is probably better to use the second algorithm shown immediately below.

The preceding algorithm allows us to search the work space in parallel for all occurrences of a given pattern, but it relies on the fact that when using "Move Activity Forward" each cell has a unique successor. Thus searches are rapid but any attempt to insert or delete characters leads to problems. We prefer to design an algorithm that will find only one instance of the pattern, but will allow easy expansion or contraction of the string. Therefore we use the organization of Fig. 6.12, with an explicit successor called out in each cell. Now we find the first occurrence of an A and mark it processed. Then we examine the cell with an entry number one greater than the entry number of the cell that held A (namely the cell with entry number 27). This cell contains a Q so we go back to search for the first unprocessed cell holding an A. This time we find the cell with entry number 39. Looking in the cell with entry number 40 we find a B and in the cell with entry number 41 we find a C. If we were searching for ABC we are through.

Now we can step back or ahead in the chain any number of steps by subtracting or adding a constant to the entry number we have. We can insert or delete as we did for the linked list above.

In a conventional memory, the time taken to search out all the

flag	list	entry #	symbol
	1	26	A

flag	list	entry #	symbol
	1	27	Q

flag	list	entry #	symbol
	1	28	M

flag	list	entry #	symbol
	1	39	A

flag	list	entry #	symbol
	1	40	B

flag	list	entry #	symbol
	1	41	C

Fig. 6.12 Organization for a SNOBOL-like string of characters.

ABC patterns is proportional to the total number of characters in the work space. Here the time is proportional to the number of occurrences of the symbol "*A*"; surely much fewer than the total number of characters.

One might say that we have given the cells "addresses" in the sense that they have unique names by which we can refer to them. But the obvious advantage is that these addresses aren't nailed down but can be rearranged or made two-dimensional, or whatever we find convenient.

AIR TRAFFIC CONTROL

The control of many airplanes in a crowded space around an airport is a very serious problem (Meilander, 1968). For each plane we predict where it will be some few seconds from now. Then the predicted position of each plane is compared with that of every other plane, and if there is an intersection, the human controller is notified. The original installation of Staran was at FAA headquarters in Knoxville, Tennessee, to solve just this problem.

Having no data whatsoever on how Goodyear handled the problem we are free to invent our own solution.

We will assign one word in the CAPP to each airplane. In that word we need to keep the following information:

1. An identifier pointing to a conventional-memory table describing the plane, its call letters and type.
2. Present X coordinate obtained from radar.
3. Present Y coordinate obtained from radar.
4. Present X velocity.
5. Present Y velocity.
6. Predicted X position.
7. Predicted Y position.
8. Present altitude.

For all planes, in parallel, we add the present X velocity to the present X position to obtain the predicted X position and repeat to get the predicted Y position.

Now we retrieve the predicted position for the first plane and using a within-limits search see if any other plane is going to be at $X_f \pm \Delta X$ (where X_f is the future X position and ΔX is some externally chosen value for the closest safe approach distance) and simultaneously at $Y_f \pm \Delta Y$ and at the same altitude. We repeat for each plane on our system and then cause to flash, for the operator's attention, any intersecting pair of planes.

The arithmetic is done in a time independent of the number of planes and the collision calculation is time proportional to N rather than N^2. This represents a significant decrease in processing time, or conversely, an increase in the number of planes that can be handled.

No word as to the outcome of the tests at Knoxville is currently available, but it should be clear that a CAPP will handle the intersection problem with dispatch.

SORTING

It has been estimated that at any given instant, half of the university computers in the world are compiling and half of the business computers are sorting.

Sorting is such an important aspect of computing that almost every general purpose computer comes with a sort package. You specify the fields and the direction of sorting from least to greatest, or greatest to least, and the canned routine does the rest. Fast sorting algorithms appear regularly in the Communications of the ACM and the Computer Journal and indeed whole books have been written on the subject.

The best sorting algorithms for conventional machines take a time proportional to $N \log N$ to sort N items. The fact that such algorithms exist is another measure of the importance that people have attached to the problem. Naive approaches take the order of N^2 steps. Consider the simplest method. Examine each element. Compare it with the smallest one found so far. If the new element is smaller, keep that one, otherwise keep the one you have. After examining all N elements, you will have the smallest one. Read it out or store it somewhere, erase that element from the array and repeat. Clearly this takes N passes through N elements or N^2 comparisons.

In a CAPP, the operation is straightforward. Search for the smallest element. For a 32 bit word with 100 nanosecond bit serial techniques, and appropriate response store organization, this will take about 3.2 μsec. Read out the element found, store it in an RAM in order of retrieval, and erase the entry from the CAPP. Repeat until the CAPP is empty. Read will take about 3.2 μsec unless we use the variable comparand search in which case reading is unnecessary since the answer is developed in the Comparand Register as we do the search. Erasing takes at most 3.2 μsec and if we implement the "next above' search it is not required either. Thus, for an optimized design, a CAPP would take 3.2 N μsecs to sort N elements. For $N > 5$, this would be faster than almost any conceivable coordinate addressed machine.

But let us probe just a bit deeper into the problem. Why are we sorting in the first place? The predominant reason for sorting is so we can then perform a merge or an update of some master file. We stream the master file past the sorted data and do inserts or replacements or what have you from the daily transactions. Given a CAPP, it is not necessary to sort at all. As the master file streams by, we ask if any changes for a record exist. If so, we do the update, and if not we go on to the next record. It should be clear that at the very worst, sorting would become insignificant given a CAPP.

TIME SHARING FRONT END

Consider the communications multiplexer or front end of a time sharing computer system. (Wald, 1973). Typically up to 50 or a 100 terminals of various speeds are connected to one side of the front end and a large central computer is attached to the other side. (See Fig. 6.13) Characters are accepted from the terminals asynchronously and collected in buffers and passed to the central machine. Simultaneously, output from user programs or the operating system is accepted and distributed to the different terminals.   Two approaches to designing the front end computer have been used in the past.   In the first, each port—the logical entity which corresponds to a phone line or hardwired line—is given enough hardware to assemble and disassemble characters.   This is necessary because almost all terminals operate in bit-serial mode and it is necessary to convert to and from internal bit parallel.   Generally an idle line is sending a continuous stream of *zeros*.   A start pulse comes first and is a logical *one*. This is followed by 8 (in some systems 5) data pulses of *ones* and *zeros* and that is in turn followed by 1, $1\frac{1}{2}$, or 2 logical *zeros* called stop pulses.   The stop pulses allow the terminal hardware to have some small variations in speed and still be ready when a new start pulse comes along.   To make matters more complicated, various terminals operate at different speeds.   A model 33 Teletype takes 110 pulses per second (called "baud") an IBM 2741 selectric typewriter requires 143.7, others take 300.   Accommodating these variations and providing the serial-parallel-serial conversion with hardware dedicated to each port costs money.   Further, the costs are linearly dependent on the number of ports to be handled simultaneously.

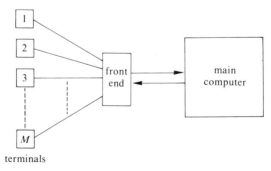

terminals

Fig. 6.13 The general layout of a time-sharing system.

The other approach is to have a mini-computer which polls the terminal lines and performs the required operations for each terminal in its own CPU. This is certainly going to be cheaper than providing hardware for each port, but it is obvious that at some point the CPU will get saturated and no more ports can be added to the system.

Let us attempt to design a CAPP to perform these functions. We will assume that the CAPP can read and write in the central computer store so that it can do buffering of one typewriter line of characters there for each port. On input, the reception of a carriage return will signal the end of a line and cause the CAPP to issue an interrupt to the central computer. On output, a carriage return will also signal the end of the line. Probably double buffering of lines for each terminal will prevent lost characters on input or momentary pauses or hiccups on output.

Consider first a single terminal sending in a character. (See Fig. 6.14). Because of inductance and capacitance on the electrical lines, the ideal time to sample the bits of the characters is in the neighborhood of half way through the bit time. If we cause a clock to run at eight times the bit rate and count up three pulses after the beginning of the start pulse and every eight pulses thereafter, we will always be sampling close to the center of each bit even though the clock and the terminal are asynchronous. After the 75th clock pulse, when we have sampled the eighth information pulse and the stop pulse has arrived, we can move the assembled character out of the character buffer word which is content addressable and store it in the line buffer which is not.

On output, we can operate synchronously. As the count reaches three modulo 8 we can transmit the next bit of the character buffer to the terminal. We will arrange that the input line from the terminal is readable as a bit of the character buffer word and that the output line to the terminal can be written as part of the character buffer word. (See Fig. 6.15).

Figure 6.16 and 6.17 show the algorithm for handling input and output.

We start in Fig. 6.16 at the place called BEGIN. First of all, we are going to process completed input characters because loss of input is more serious than delay of output. We find a cell (if any exist) that

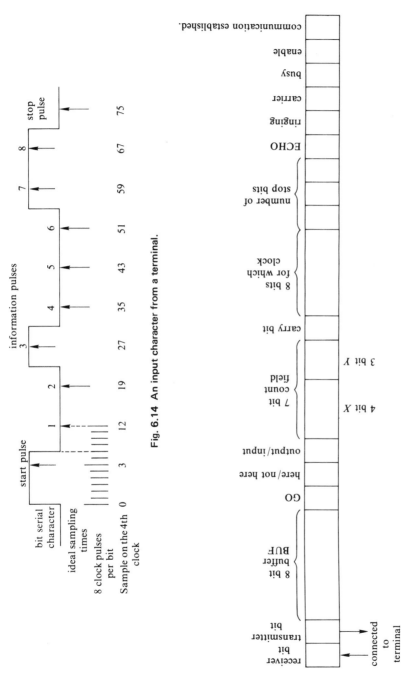

Fig. 6.14 An input character from a terminal.

Fig. 6.15 The character buffer word.

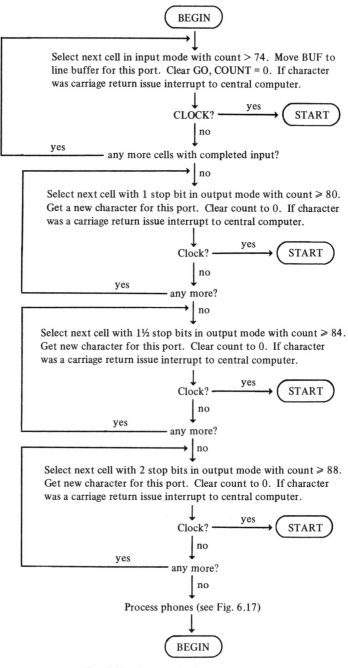

Fig. 6.16 Main routine for front end.

is in input mode with a count >74. We use the simplest greater than search to keep costs down. (We allow for greater than in case we are a little late getting here.) We move the completed input character from BUF (which is content addressable) to that port's line buffer (which is not) and clear the GO bit and the COUNT field to zero. If the character was a carriage return, indicating the end of the line, we issue an interrupt to the central computer and if this is a double buffered system, switch over to work on the other buffer.

If there has been a clock flag raised indicating that some one of the several clocks we permit on the system has emitted a pulse, we go off to START in Fig. 6.17. If no clock has times out we repeat,

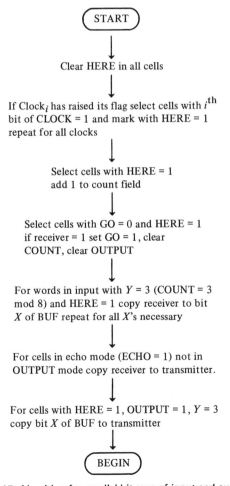

START

Clear HERE in all cells

If Clock$_i$ has raised its flag select cells with i^{th} bit of CLOCK = 1 and mark with HERE = 1 repeat for all clocks

Select cells with HERE = 1 add 1 to count field

Select cells with GO = 0 and HERE = 1 if receiver = 1 set GO = 1, clear COUNT, clear OUTPUT

For words in input with Y = 3 (COUNT = 3 mod 8) and HERE = 1 copy receiver to bit X of BUF repeat for all X's necessary

For cells in echo mode (ECHO = 1) not in OUTPUT mode copy receiver to transmitter.

For cells with HERE = 1, OUTPUT = 1, Y = 3 copy bit X of BUF to transmitter

BEGIN

Fig. 6.17 Algorithm for parallel bit scan of input and output.

cleaning up input characters until they are all processed. Then we begin to work on the ports in output mode that have finished their present character and need a new one. If the particular terminal uses one stop bit we wait for a count of 80; if $1\frac{1}{2}$ stop bits, a count of 84; and if 2 stop bits, a count of 88. We get a new character for this port (from the random access memory), clear its count to zero, and check to see if the character was a carriage return and if it was, we issue an interrupt to the central computer and switch buffers if the system is double buffered. Once again, after each output character has been processed, we check to see if any clock flags have gone to one, and go off to START if any have.

After all output characters of all three lengths of stop bit have been taken care of, we process the phones (see below) and then go back to BEGIN to look for completed input characters. If there is nothing to do, the algorithm of Fig. 6.16 forms an idle loop waiting for a clock flag or some other action to be performed.

In this routine the content addressability of the cells is used in each selection, thus speeding up the operation considerably.

The routine of Fig. 6.17 is entered whenever one or more of the free running clocks on the system indicates that one of its time periods has gone by. This routine copies in bits from the lines to the terminals and sends out bits to the terminals in output mode. There is one clock for each different baud rate supported by the system. We assume eight clocks for the sake of argument. Each clock runs at eight times the baud rate of the particular kind of terminal it is supposed to control. In each port's character buffer word there are eight bits called the clock bits. Software will, upon identifying the terminal type, set one of the bits in this field of each port's character buffer word. Thus, up to eight different baud rates can be supported.

At START (Fig. 6.17) we first clear the HERE flag of all cells and then for each clock that has raised its flag, we select all those cells using that baud rate and mark them with HERE = 1. Since it takes a finite time to process characters in Fig. 6.16, more than one clock may have its flag up at a time. Any number of clocks may contribute to the set of cells to be processed on this pass.

Now we select those cells, inputting or outputting with HERE = 1 and add one to their count fields since another one of their clock periods has gone by. Again, we use a slow algorithm taking $9N$ probes.

Next we select all cells with HERE = 1 and the GO bit equal to zero (meaning they are not now in the process of inputting a character) and if their receiver bit is one (a start pulse is arriving) we set GO = 1 indicating that we are now receiving a character. We then clear the count field and the OUTPUT bit to zero. If the system was outputting a character it will be lost. We feel it is more important to listen to the user than to talk to him. Other decisions could have been made.

For all words with GO = 1, with HERE = 1 and $Y = 3$ (Y is the residue modulo 8 of the count field: the three low order bits and X is the other four bits of the count field) we are half way through a bit time so we copy the contents of the receiver bit into the Xth bit of the BUF field. This is not done for $X = 0$ since that represents the start bit, but it is done for all other X's (1 through 8) that we encounter; each X done separately since the bits involved are different.

For all cells in echoplex mode (the front end echos the input back to the terminal) that are *not* in output mode and have $Y = 3$, we copy the receiver bit to the transmitter bit. We do this once every pass because it is easier to do it than to test to see if it needs to be done.

Finally, we select those cells in output mode with HERE = 1 and $Y = 3$ and copy bit X of BUF to the transmitter bit. Once again, this must be done for each value of X separately but in this case for $X = 0$ we copy a *one* to the transmitter to act as the start bit. For $X > 8$ we copy a zero to the transmitter to act as the stop bit or bits.

This completes the bit scan so control is given to the main routine at BEGIN to see if any input characters are completed or output characters are depleted.

Timing this routine is somewhat difficult but assuming our usual 0.1 μsec bit-serial CAPP we have a 0.5 μsec to set, select, and write HERE per clock and we will assume only one clock is active. Adding 1 to the count field takes about 6.3 μsec, handling *new* inputs takes 1.2 μsec. About 0.5 μsec for each value of X is necessary and assuming all 8 are done we need 4 μsec to input a bit, 0.4 μsec to echo, and another 4 μsec to output a bit. This implies very nearly 16 μsec per pass through the bit scan algorithm of Fig. 6.16. Supposing we have clocks for 110, 143.7, and 300 baud then we have 554 X 8 or about 400 clock flags raised per second. At 16 μsec per flag this would occupy about 70,000 μsec or 70 milliseconds per second leaving 930 milliseconds per second to move characters back and forth between the character buffer words and the central computer's memory. Each such move involves a search for greater than (say one μsec), a read from content addressable store, and an indirect write to the RAM (or an indirect read from the RAM and a write to content addressable store); plus clearing GO and COUNT (say another μsec) for a rough total of 10 to 20 μsec, depending on the character-manipulating capabilities of the central memory. Taking the worst case, we could process $\frac{930,000}{20}$ or better than 45,000 characters per second.

If we assume all terminals are 300 baud (30 characters/sec) and are running flat out, we are limited to *only* 1500 terminals on this particular front end computer. (Note especially that the bit scan is not dependent on the number of ports to be processed.)

Processing phone calls and hangups is shown in Fig. 6.18. This is left to last in Fig. 6.16 because it seems more important to talk to the people already connected than to connect new people. Five bits

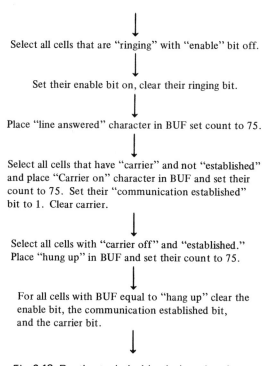

Select all cells that are "ringing" with "enable" bit off.

Set their enable bit on, clear their ringing bit.

Place "line answered" character in BUF set count to 75.

Select all cells that have "carrier" and not "established" and place "Carrier on" character in BUF and set their count to 75. Set their "communication established" bit to 1. Clear carrier.

Select all cells with "carrier off" and "established." Place "hung up" in BUF and set their count to 75.

For all cells with BUF equal to "hang up" clear the enable bit, the communication established bit, and the carrier bit.

Fig. 6.18 Routine to deal with telephone interfaces.

of the character buffer word are set aside to deal with the data sets. We assume that the carrier bit goes to *one* when the carrier changes state from ON to OFF or vice versa. First we "pick up the receiver" for all phones ringing and inform the central computer via a "phone answered" character that this has happened. When the carrier is detected, we place the port in "communication established" mode and again notify the central machine via a "carrier on" character.

When the central machine sends over a "hang up" character or when we detect a user disconnect via loss of carrier, we hang up the phone and if it is a user action inform the central computer.

In summary, then, we find that we can substitute the parallel processing ability of a CAPP for a good deal of hardware. Few people probably need a front-end capable of handling 1500 terminals, but it is nice to know it can be done inexpensively if we ever need one.

A RELAXATION PROBLEM

There is a large number of physical problems in which the conservation of something flowing across a region is of interest. (Lamport, 1974). Examples of such problems include heat flow, incompressable fluid flow, electrical potentials, and many others. One way of solving such problems is via what is called a relaxation method. Boundary conditions are fixed and then at each point in the surface or volume to be studied we estimate a new value of the variable of concern by averaging the values displayed by its immediate neighbors. Thus, in Fig. 6.19 the new value of the variable at cell i, j will be:

$$V_{i,j} = \tfrac{1}{4} (V_{i,j-1} + V_{i,j+1} + V_{i-1,j} + V_{i+1,j})$$

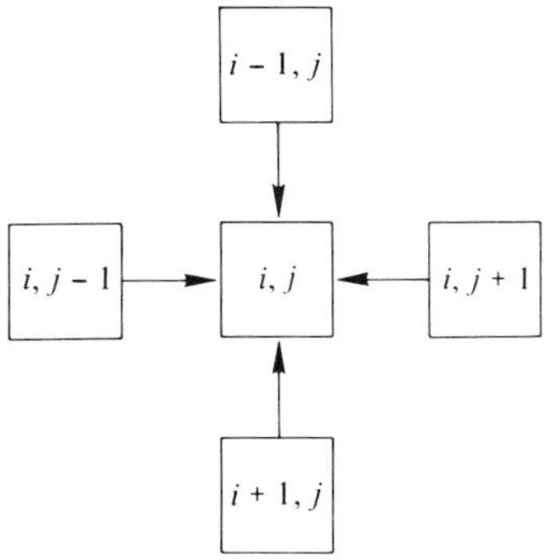

Fig. 6.19 Part of a square array.

This averaging is repeated for all cells of the space many times until stability is reached and the values no longer change. Obviously, this is slow. Illiac IV was designed as an array processor to solve just this sort of problem. Illiac IV has 64 processors arranged in an 8 × 8 grid.

Let us see how we might go about solving a relaxation problem using a CAPP. We will specify that response activity can be shifted North, South, East, and West one square. Each cell will contain the following fields:

B – this cell is part of a fixed boundary condition and its value is not to be changed.

V – the current value of the Variable of concern.

T – a temporary register for computation.

C – carry register.

N – a flag to hold a copy of a neighbor's bit.

Our scheme is as follows: For all non-boundary cells we clear T and then add to the T of each cell one quarter of the value of V of the cell immediately to its left. Then we add in $\frac{1}{4} V_{i-1,j}$ and then $\frac{1}{4} V_{i,j+1}$ and finally $\frac{1}{4} V_{i+1,j}$. This gives the new value for $V_{i,j}$ and so we can copy the contents of every T field into that cell's own V field; or if we want to save doing the copy, we simply interchange the names of the T and V fields.

The fundamental technique for the addition of the contents of one cell to its neighbor is: For all cells with a *one* in the ith bit of their V fields, shift activity right and write N equal *one*. Now add N, C, and the local T_{i+2} to get a new T_{i+2} (the plus two divides the sum by four), a new Carry, and clear N for the next stage.

Assuming N and C are incorporated in the response store, to set, select and shift right still takes three probes and it will take two more to read out and modify T_{i+2}. This is at best five probes per bit and we must add in $4B$ bits, or endure $20B$ probes. Supposing B to be 20 bits, that is 400 probes.

Illiac IV can be adding 64 cells at a time and it needs to add from four directions, just as we do. Supposing an Illiac IV cycle time is the same as our bit probe time then in a unit of time Illiac IV does one iteration for 16 cells (= $\frac{64}{4}$) whereas in our CAPP in 400 units of time we can do one pass for every cell. If there are as many as 400 × 16 = 6400 points on the grid (cells) then our machine is faster than Illiac. If there are fewer, Illiac wins.

It is interesting to contrast the relative complexities of the two computers; theirs and ours.

USES IN CONVENTIONAL COMPUTERS

Perhaps the best known application of CAPP's is to the short circuiting of address look up in the IBM 360/67.

A memory address consists of three parts in this machine called the segment, page, and line. Each user has a segment table and several page tables. A program is broken into logical segments. These in turn are divided into pages. Each page resides in a page frame when it is in residence in central storage but at different times it may occupy different page frames.

Address calculation proceeds as follows:

The user specifies an address of

$$S_i P_j L_k.$$

The ith entry of this users segment table corresponding to segment S_i is retrieved and the information stored there tells the machine where the page table for this segment is stored. Now the jth entry of this page table is retrieved and that tells the machine in which page-frame it will find page P_j of segment S_i. Using this page frame address as a base, we offset from it by L_k to find the final actual address α we were searching for. This requires a minimum of three memory probes to get any piece of data.

To make this faster, what was done on the 67 was to store the most recently used addresses in a small (16 word) associative memory. We store $S_i P_j$ and α the final page-frame address in one word. Now when an address comes up, we look first in the AM to see if it has already been translated into a physical address. If it has, then $\alpha + Lk$ is sent to the memory address register and the data is retrieved in one probe instead of three. Note particularly that only addresses and not data are kept in this AM.

When a hit on the AM is made that word is moved to the "top" of the AM which has the ability to function like a pushdown stack. If a new unknown address comes along the first time it must be translated by looking up in segment and page table. Then it is added to the top of the AM stack together with its translation. This forces the bottom element of the stack to be "pushed off" the end of the stack. Since each time an address is referenced, it gets promoted to the head of the stack; it is the least recently used (LRU) address that gets bumped off. Using this algorithm and a stack of eight words long, approximately 80% of all addresses were found in the AM. This means that 80% of the time, we need one memory reference to get a datum, and the remaining 20% of the time we need three. This averages out to $0.8 + 0.6 = 1.4$ references which is less than half of what it would be without the AM.

The next step beyond what is described above is to store the data in the AM as well as the label (SPL) and the address. Given a high speed AM this could serve very nicely as a cache similar to the 360/85 or the 370/195 and short circuit most all main memory references. Reading from a datum for a second time is thus sped up immensely.   Writing a datum can be done as a "write-through;" that is, always updating the main-memory copy at the same time as the AM copy is updated; or it can be done only when the word is ready to be pushed out of the AM.

Write-through is slow. On the other hand, there is always an up-to-date copy in main store for use by another processor, say the I/O processor. Secondly, with write-through, the management of the AM is slightly simplified. Any word in the AM is an equally good candidate for elimination and this can be accomplished by simple overwriting.   There is already an up-to-date copy in main store, so no "roll-out" is required.

Perhaps a good compromise would be to set up a "writing queue" which would be designed to copy all changes to the words of the AM to main store as fast as it could, but to have the capacity to buffer somewhat so that the CPU didn't have to wait for the writing to be completed before going on.

The English Electric KDF.9 had such a queue but it was insufficiently interlocked and if you really wanted to reference an item after storing it, you made sure to store it *twice,* thus driving one copy out of the queue into core. But this is getting a bit far from applications of CAPP's.

DISCOVERING CONTIGUOUS AREAS

Consider the following problem: we have a two dimensional surface and we wish to find the set of all points that are "connected to" a given starting point. By connected to, we mean that they are either neighbors, or neighbors of neighbors, or, etc. In particular, suppose we wish to find the extent of a certain *red object*. We cannot just request "all red points" because there may be more than one non-contiguous red thing present.

We first select one point known to be on the red object. We let this point "broadcast activity" to all its red neighbors. We repeat this broadcasting until no new points are activated.

Activation of the neighbors can be accomplished by using two flags.

1. Select all "active"cells. (Flag A = 1)
2. Move activity east.
3. Write 1 in flag B.
4. Repeat steps 1–3 for North, West, and South.
5. Select all cells with 1 in flag B.
6. If none, STOP. Otherwise,
7. Write 0 in flag B.
8. Discard cells that are not red.
9. Write 1 in flag A.
10. Repeat steps 1–10.

If we intended to use the CAPP a large percentage of the time in this form of contagion-propagation we might add the special circuit of Fig. 6.20 and replace the above algorithm with the following:

1. Select starting cell.
2. Broadcast.
3. Discard non red cells.
4. Repeat steps 2 and 3 often enough for activity to reach all parts of the net.

Another interesting application of contagion is what has been called the "prairie fire" technique of classifying shapes. We begin

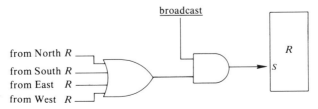

Fig. 6.20 A special circuit to facilitate contagion. When the broadcast line is energized any cell whose neighbor is active will become active.

with the boundary of an object active. We let this activity "burn" its way in toward the center and where opposing lines of "fire" meet and extinguish each other, we note the location and time of each cell at which fire meets fire. It is claimed that from these lines and clumps of "burnout" cells it is possible to reconstruct the original boundary by reversing the process. Whether or not that is the case is not of immediate interest here, we are more concerned with "how to" than "why."

First, let us find the "boundary" of the object. We assume that the entire contiguous area has been marked in flag A by a process similar to the one just described. We define a cell to be *on the boundary* if at least one of its neighbors is not part of object.

The steps are:

1. Select all cells not part of the object (flag $A = 0$).
2. Move activity East.
3. Write 1 in flag B.
4. Repeat 2 and 3 for North, South and West.
5. Select all cells not part of the object (flag $A = 0$).
6. Write flag $B = 0$.

This leaves exactly the boundary cells with flag $B = 1$.

To find the cells that will be the "burnout" cells, we need the following special bits:

—flag $A = 1$ means the cell is part of the object.
—flag $P = 1$ means the cell has been processed.
—flag $C = 1$ means this is a "burnout" cell.
—flag $B = 1$ this is a boundary cell.
—counter—two bit field.
—time—perhaps 10 bits to record the iteration number.

Operation proceeds as:

1. Select all cells on the boundary (flag $B = 1$) and mark as processed. (Flag $P = 1$)
2. Clear counter field of all cells.
3. Move activity East.
4. Discard any cells that are processed already or not part of the object.
5. Add one to the contents of the counter field.
6. Repeat steps 3, 4, and 5 for North, West, and South.

7. Write flag $B = 0$, everywhere.
8. Select any cell with counter equal to one.
9. Write flag $B = 1$, flag $P = 1$ making these cells the new boundary.
10. If no boundary cells left, exit.
11. Select cells with counter greater than one (two or more fire cells "converged" on each of these cells).
12. Write flag $C = 1$, write iteration number in time field.
13. Go to step 1.

It is interesting to note that any number of bounded areas or "objects" can be treated simultaneously because the initial marking of the boundaries as "processed" in step 1 effectively isolates one area from another.   Therefore, a whole picture can be done in one fell swoop.

After all the burnout cells have been marked, content addressability once again comes to the rescue in case one wishes to read the pattern of burnout cells out of the array for storage or some other kind of processing.   In that case it would be convenient if each cell contained a field with a unique identifying number, or better yet, two fields i and j with the array coordinates of the cell stored herein.

GEAR RATIOS FOR AN ORRERY

Not all readers will wish to design fancy astronomical clocks, but we include this example of the versatility of CAPP's for the fun of it.

As an example of an application of CAPP's to numerical calculations, we consider the problem of selecting gears for a miniature planetarium.   A planetarium built into a clock is called an Orrery and is named after the Earl of Cork and Orrery.   The first one was built by Thomas Tompion and "Honest" George Graham in about the year 1705.   We wish to design a train of three pairs of gears (see Fig. 6.21).   We will restrict our attention to three pairs of gears for simplicity of construction.   Further, we will restrict ourselves to using stock gears.   Stock Drive Products makes a set of molded plastic gears with constant pitch and pressure angle that sell for under $1 each.   Specially cut gears with unusual numbers of teeth *are* available at a surcharge of around $50 each.   Therefore it is a nice idea to use standard gears if at all possible.   The set of $1 gears consists of 40 different tooth numbers: all numbers between 18 and 40 plus various

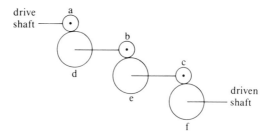

Fig. 6.21 A train of three pairs of gears: ad, be, and cf. The ratio of the speeds of the driven shaft to the speed of the drive shaft is abc/def.

other numbers of teeth up to and including 120. (Twelve factors: 2,3,5,7,11,13,17,19,23,29,31, and 37 are used in the set of forty gears but this information has not turned out to be useful.)

We wish then to calculate a gear train that will take a one revolution per week synchronous electric motor (also available off the shelf) and end up with a shaft that turns once in 365.242198 days; one year. Of course, the probability of hitting exactly on a 52.177457 to 1 ratio with only six gears is vanishingly small, so we will be satisfied with whatever ratio comes closest.

The conventional brute force way of handling this problem would be to write six nested DO loops which would select all 40^6 = 4,096,000,000 combinations of six gears, compute the product of the three ratios:

$$R = \frac{a \cdot b \cdot c}{d \cdot e \cdot f} = \frac{a}{d} \cdot \frac{b}{e} \cdot \frac{c}{f}$$

and compare the result R with the best achieved so far. The better of the two would be preserved and some several hours later the best answer would be available.

Our approach will be to use a CAPP of 40^3 or 64,000 cells. We will *consider* these cells to be arranged in a cube 40 cells on a side. Each cell has five fields: $a, b, c,$ product, temporary, and some flags.

Beginning with all cells initially blank we wish to first arrange that each cell will contain the product of three gear tooth numbers such that each cell corresponds to a different choice of the three gears a, b and c. This will represent all the possible numerators of the ratio (see Fig. 6.22).

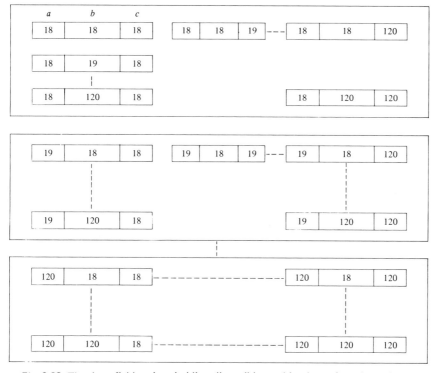

Fig. 6.22 The three fields *a, b, c,* holding all possible combinations of tooth numbers.

If the CAPP was built as a three dimensional cube, the method of getting to the condition of Fig. 6.22 would be to select all cells for which $X = 1$ and write 18 in their *a*-field. For $X = 2$, we write 19 in the *a*-field . . . for $X = 40$, we write 120 in their *a* field. Then for $Y = 1$, we write 18 in the *b*-field, . . . , for $Y = 40$, we write 120 in the *b*-field. For $Z = 1$, we write 18 in the *c*-field, . . . , for $Z = 40$ we write 120 in the *c*-field. This would take a total of 3 × 40 or 120 steps.

Given a less specialized CAPP we must fall back on somewhat slower methods. We arrange, probably via software, for 3 counters that count modulo 40 with the overflow from C serving as input to B and the overflow from B serving as input to A. Now we expend 64,000 steps of the following:

1. Select first empty cell.
2. Write counters ABC into fields abc.

3. Add 1 to counter C.

4. Repeat until A overflows.

Now we select all cells with a-field = 1 and write 18 in their a-fields, etc., for 120 steps (3 × 40) until we are again at the situation of Fig. 6.22.

Given 2^{18} cells with addresses stored in the cell, we could break the address into three parts and proceed as if the array were in truth three dimensional. In any event, we get to the point at which each cell has a different set of three tooth numbers stored in a, b, and c.

We multiply in parallel the contents of the a-field of each cell by the contents of the b-field of that cell and store the result in the *temp* field. Next, we multiply in parallel the contents of the c-field by the contents of the *temp* field and store that result in the *product* field. This requires two multiplications rather than 64,000. Note that we have postponed the multiplications as long as possible since they are relatively slow, so that all cells could be done in parallel.

We have 64,000 cells which between them contain all possible numerators of the ratio. Not all cells will have different products, however, since there are six possible ways to arrange three gears. But not only rearrangement produces duplicates. While it is true that

$$40 \times 20 \times 60 = 20 \times 40 \times 60$$

it is also true that

$$40 \times 20 \times 60 = 120 \times 20 \times 20$$

so that many fewer than $64,000/6 \simeq 10,000$ different products are present. The exact number of different products is not known to this author.

We select the smallest uninvestigated product P_i; in the first pass it will be 18^3 or 5832 and for each cell in parallel we compute the product divided by P_i (or multiplied by $1/P_i$ if you prefer) and store the answer in the *temp* field. From these ratios, we select (associatively of course) the one closest to the desired ratio of 52.177457. We then take the next smallest P_i and repeat.

The best new ratio is compared with the old and the closer of the two is preserved. This is repeated some 5 or 10,000 times until all different products have been used. If we have a 3-dimensional CAPP, we have consumed the order of 10,000 steps. If we have a "conventional" CAPP we have used the order of 100,000 steps. Either of these numbers is to be compared with 4 billion steps for a von Neumann machine.

SUMMARY

We have presented some applications of CAPP's and have tried to show that they span numerical as well as logical problems. In addition to the ones we have discussed here, other people have looked at other problems.

Many other applications of CAPP's have been suggested. Wesley (1969) discusses the fast Fourier transform in a CAPP, Erwin (1970) queues interrupts, while Estrin (1963a) covers several applications. Gilmore (1971) proposes to solve partial differential equations, and to perform parallel compilation (1965a, b). Database management is an obvious if complicated application (Goodyear, 1972c) and several people have investigated parallel picture processing (Fuller, 1965b; Kruse, 1973; Stillman, 1971).

7 | DISTRIBUTED HARDWARE

In this chapter we will look at some of the ways hardware can be put together to provide the logical function we wish to have distributed over the memory. Some of these methods have been briefly mentioned in previous chapters. We will collect these here and explore the other methods that have been suggested in the literature.

RESPONSE RESOLUTION

As discussed in Chapter 3, we require a select-first-responder so that we can separate two cells that, by some mischance, have identical contents. The then existing methods were discussed in Foster (1968). Let us summarize them here.

In the Goodyear-Rome Air Development Center 2048 word associative memory, the response store bits are copied 32 at a time into a scanning register. If all 32 are zero, the next block of 32 is obtained. When a block is found which is not all zero, the register is scanned left to right for the first ONE. The combination of the block number and the bit number form a word address and conventional coincident current techniques are used to read out the word. If block transfer and bit scanning have equal speeds, the time to find a responder will be proportional to $N^{1/2}$, where N is the number of words in the memory.

Another method of response resolution involves scanning of an address field stored with each word. All responders are ORed onto the output bus which has two lines per bit of the address field. (See Lewin's method described in Chapter 9.)

Each word is arranged to have a unique number (its address) stored permanently in its address field. If there are two or more responders, then at least one bit of the address field will have both the ZERO and ONE line energized. Pick the most significant such address bit and reset the flags of all words which have a ONE in this position. Repeat until no address bit has both ZERO and ONE lines energized. There will then be only one responder and it may be gated onto the output bus and read without ambiguity.

This method has the advantage that relatively little logic is required at each word of the memory, but it has two disadvantages. First, the memory must be searched up to b times for each read operation, where b is the number of bits in the address field. This represents a slowdown in operating speed that could be very significant. Second, there is the problem of storing the addresses in the address field of each word.

For a volatile memory, such as flip-flops or cryotrons, one must consider the problem of recovery from a disaster. An alternate method of selecting a word must be provided. True, the disaster recovery scheme could be quite slow, but nontheless it will require logic at each word at least as complex as the cascaded OR presented below. If, on the other hand, the address information is "wired in," we are faced with two aspects of the fabrication problem: 1) the mask of address connections must be different for each word, raising the cost of the memory, and 2) a great attractiveness of associative memories for mass fabrication techniques is that a "faulty" word may be bypassed by giving its "name" to another element of the array. This would permit vastly improved yields and hence much lower costs. "Wiring in" an address would defeat this approach.

ITERATIVE METHODS

The "chain bit" has been discussed at length in the literature and appears to be an attractive solution for cryogenic associative memories (Rosin, 1962). Its approximate equivalent for integrated-circuit technology is the cascaded OR network shown in Fig. 7.1.

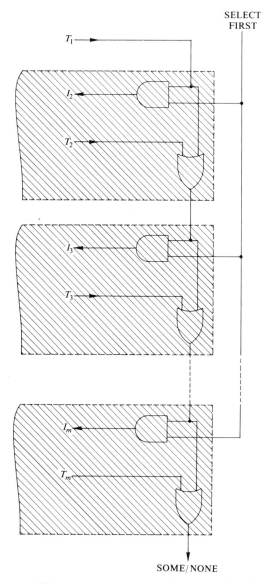

Fig. 7.1 The cascaded OR method of resolving multiple responders. T_i is the output of the ith tag bit. I_i is the "inhibit" line to the ith response store.

This has the advantage that every word has identical structure (except, perhaps, the first and last of the array), which will surely reduce costs; but it has the disadvantage that if there are N words in the memory, and the first one is a responder, the signal must propagate through N gates each with its inherent delay.

Given a delay of even one nanosecond per gate, it requires only a 1000-word array to generate a delay of one microsecond, and a million words would take one millisecond to settle down. An equivalent circuit using ANDs instead of ORs is mentioned by Weinstein (1963).

What is required of a priority circuit is that when word w is a responder, then words $w + 1$, $w + 2$, ... may be inhibited from "responding." One obviously impractical suggestion would be to have a 1-input OR at word 2, a 2-input OR at word 3, and, in general, a $(w - 1)$ input OR at word w. Fan-in and fan-out considerations lead to immediate discard. The circuit of Fig. 7.2 is suggested as a compromise between the above and the cascaded OR circuit. (Foster, 1968.) In Fig. 7.2 the T_i line carries a logical ONE if the flag of the ith word is set.

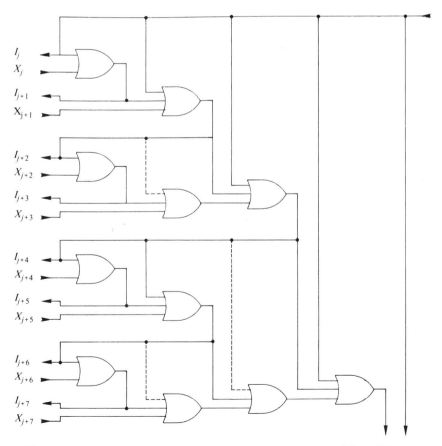

Fig. 7.2 A priority determination circuit with short delay constructed from OR gates.

If the ith word is not the "first" responder the circuit will put a logical ONE on line I_i, inhibiting read-out of that word. If there are 2^n words in the memory this circuit will have $n + 1$ levels. The worst-case delay will occur when the "first" and "last" word in the array are both responders. The signal must propagate upwards in the tree through n levels and then back down through $n - 1$ levels. This gives $(2n - 1)$-unit delays. The number of gates required may be calculated as follows.

As is well known, a full binary tree of $n + 1$ levels will have

$$2^{n+1} - 1$$

gates in total. But in the circuit of Fig. 7.2 only every second word has a gate on the bottom layer of the tree. This represents a lack of 2^{n-1} gates compared with a full tree. Thus this circuit requires a total of

$$2^{n+1} - 1 - 2^{n-1} = 3 * 2^{n-1} - 1$$

gates, or about $1\frac{1}{2}$ gates per word. Maximum fan-in is three and maximum fan-out is n. For a million-word memory n is 20. The circuits are not identical at each word but are repetitive in blocks of 2, 4, 8, ... words if the connections indicated by the dotted lines are included. The circuit has the further advantage that all connections can be made without crossovers.

A one million word priority circuit constructed from gates with a ten ns delay per stage would have a worst-case settling time of $10 \times \{(2 * 20) - 1\}$ or 390 ns.

The above method generates what is called an "inhibit" vector which consists of a string of *zeros* followed by a string of *ones* with

Response Store Vector	Inhibit Vector	Pointer Vector
0	0	0
0	0	0
0	0	0
0	0	0
1	0	1
1	1	0
0	1	0
0	1	0
0	1	0
1	1	0
0	1	0

Fig. 7.3 The response store vector is the collection of *ones* and *zeros* put out by the tag bits of the response store. The inhibit vector, or *I* vector, is a string of *zeros* followed by a string of *ones*. The pointer vector has one *one* opposite the first responder.

the transition taking place immediately after the earliest responder.
(See Fig. 7.3).   A much more organized and more efficient scheme
for generating an I vector is proposed by Anderson in a recent paper
(Anderson, 1974).   Consider the tree of Fig. 7.4.   In the example

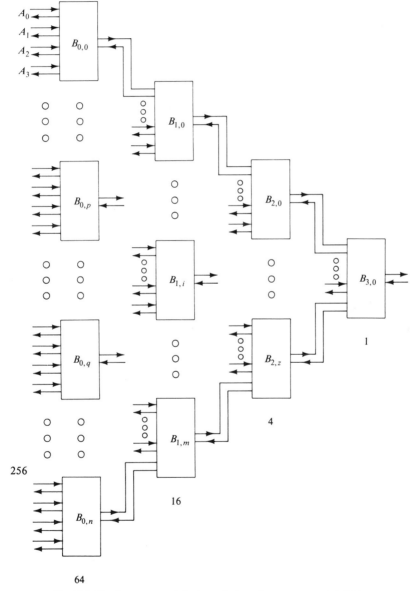

Fig. 7.4 Block structure of Anderson's trees for response resolution.

shown, each block has five pairs of lines. One pair comes in from higher up in the tree and the other four go out to lower points of the tree. Figure 7.5 shows the circuit Anderson calls the "I-Generator" block. The $A_{00} - A_{11}$ lines represent inputs of activity from four lower locations in the tree; four tag bits or four blocks, depending on the level. If any of these A bits are *one* then the A line going up the tree is activated. The I lines are inhibit lines. Inhibition can come down from on high or it may be generated by a local activity.

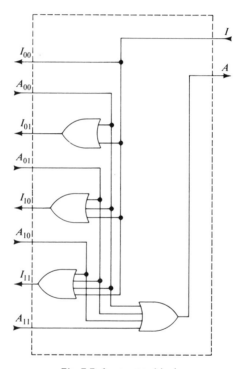

Fig. 7.5 *I*-generator block.

With 256 inputs, Anderson's scheme requires 85 blocks or 340 gates and a worst-case propagation delay of seven gate times. Maximum fan-in shown in four and maximum fan-out as shown is ten for the I_{01}, I_{10} and I_{11} lines from the top-most block. This fan-out is $1 + 3(L - 1)$ where L is the number of levels.

If, as might seem reasonable, these I_{00} lines are buffered with a driver-type gate so that loading and long lines don't degrade the signals, then the number of gates required goes to 425.

If as shown in Fig. 7.6 and 7.7, we use three input gates rather than

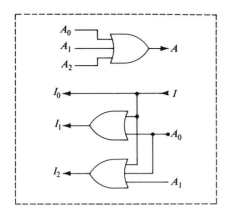

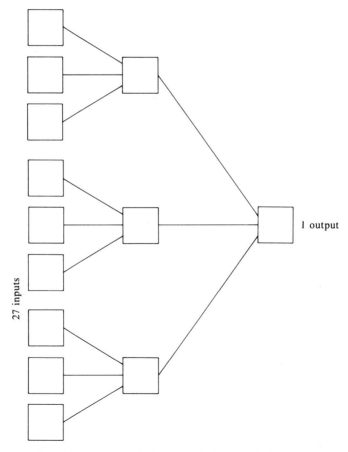

Fig. 7.6 A large unit with 27 inputs made from 13 blocks, and the building block made with gates with a fan-in of 3.

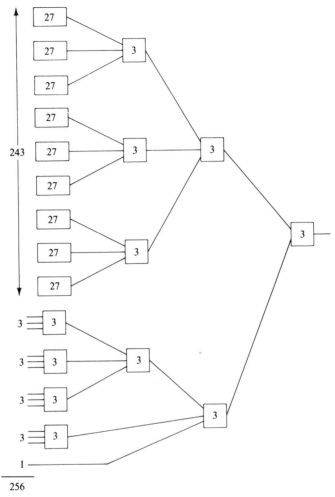

Fig. 7.7 The irregular tree built with 3 input gate building blocks to generate an *I* vector for 256 inputs.

four, we require 384 gates, nine delays and a maximum fan-out of nine, counting the I line that must be driven.

It should be emphasized that the major advantages of Anderson's are 1) shorter delay and 2) a regular structure well adapted to LSI fabrication. Anderson also discusses two other vectors in addition to the *I* vector we looked at above. The first of these is the *P* or pointer vector which consists of all zeros except one *one* pointing to the "first" responder. Clearly, the simplest way to generate *P* from *I* is shown in Fig. 7.8.

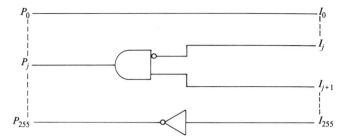

Fig. 7.8 A simple way of deriving the Pointer vector from the Inhibition vector.

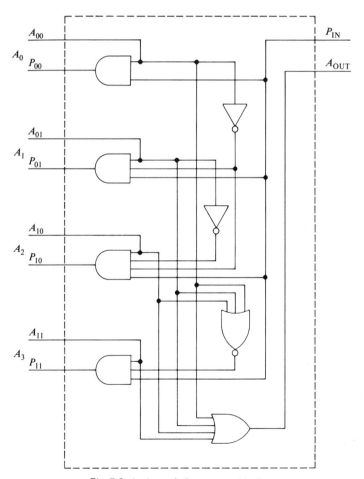

Fig. 7.9 Anderson's P-generator block.

If we assume that the inversion of I_j is available from the gate that generates I_j, then this requires 255 extra gates for a 256-bit vector (P_0 is identical to I_0). This then requires 595 gates to generate a 256-bit P-vector with four input gates. If we assume that we must generate the negation separately we need another 254 gates or 849 gates by this method.

In Fig. 7.9 Anderson shows a P-generator block that has eight gates per block and therefore with 85 blocks requires 680 gates and seven gate delays. The P_{in} line of the highest block of the pyramid is *enabled* when we wish to generate the pointer and *disabled* otherwise.

The other vector to be considered here is the "address of the first responder." Anderson adds the gates of Fig. 7.10 to the block of

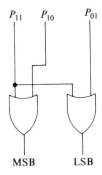

Fig. 7.10 Address generation from P-vector.

7.9 and by "wireoring" lines together as shown in Fig. 7.11 generates the address.

Koo (1970) uses the block of Fig. 7.12 and the connections of Fig. 7.13 to generate an address.

COUNTING RESPONDERS

As noted above, Kaplan early proposed an analog method of counting the approximate number of responders to a search and a slower "scan and count" instruction to obtain the exact number of responders.

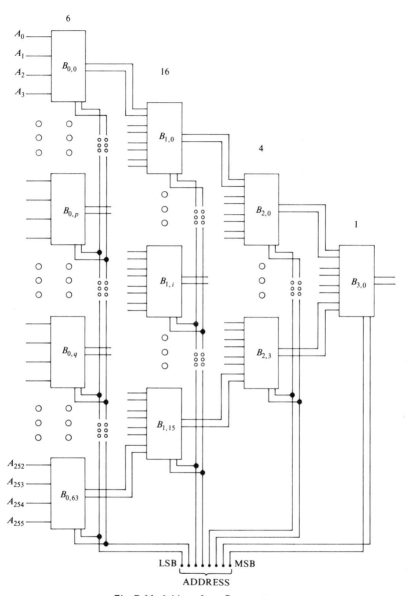

Fig. 7.11 Address from P-generator.

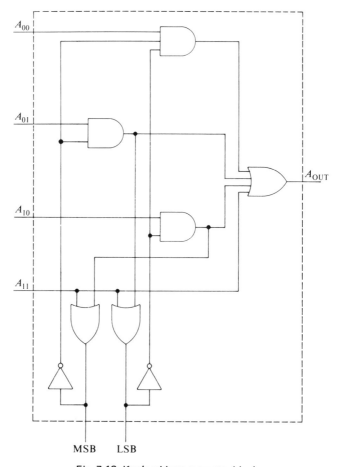

Fig. 7.12 Koo's address generator block.

The next serious attempt to design a circuit for counting responders was described in two internal memoranda at Goodyear
Aerospace (Favor, 1964; and Hill, 1965).

The method favored by Favor was to use full adders to establish
the least significant bit of the count (See Fig. 7.14). Each full adder
has three inputs and two outputs; the sum and the carry. The two
bits of the output can represent in weighted binary the four possible
states of the input (zero, one, two, or three of the input lines asserted). Figure 7.15 shows a typical full adder.

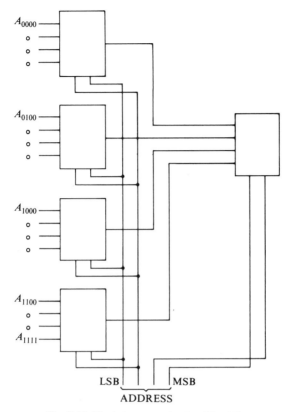

Fig. 7.13 Koo's tree organization (N = 16).

The mechanism of Fig. 7.14 works as follows. The least significant bit of the sum will be *one* if there is an odd number of *ones* in the input. But the sum output of a full-adder is *one* just when one or three of its inputs are *one*. Further, an odd number of odd numbers makes an odd number. That takes care of the least significant bit. The carry outputs (a – g) of the least significant bit pyramid represent pairs of inputs in the *one* state. We sum these pairs up in the second pyramid and if there is an odd number of pairs of inputs then the second bit of the sum is one. The rest of the bits are derived similarly.

Diminished powers of two ($2^n - 1$) inputs generate trees that utilize full adders fully. Consider a single full adder. It has three

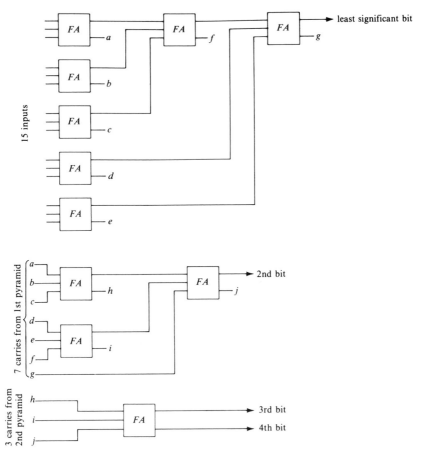

Fig. 7.14 The pyramid method of generating the count of the number of responders in an *AM*. *FA* is a full adder.

inputs. Let them be the carry inputs from another pyramid. That one can have three full adders in it. Therefore, if we have x input lines we have $(x - 1)/2$ full adders needed or conversely, with y full adders we can sum up $2y + 1$ lines. So 3 full adders have $3 \cdot 2 + 1 = 7$ inputs. Seven full adders have 15 inputs, 15 adders have 31 inputs. In general, we can handle any diminished power of two $(2^n - 1)$ using up all the inputs of the full adders.

To discover how many adders are required, we note that we want

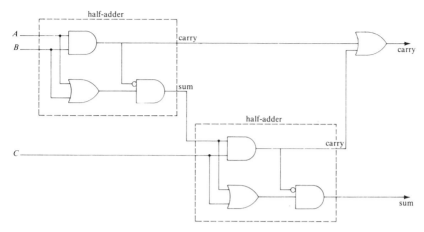

Fig. 7.15 A full adder built up from two half adders.

to reduce $2^n - 1$ input lines to n output lines. Each full adder has three input lines and two output lines (sum and carry), thereby "using up" one line. Since we wish to "use up" $2^n - 1 - n$ lines, we need just that many full adders. For example, with 255 cells we have an 8-bit output register. 255 – 8 is 247 full adders required. Approximately speaking, one full adder is needed per cell to count the number of responders.

To calculate the number of gate delays necessary to generate the count, we proceed as follows. One full adder has unit delay and three inputs. Seven inputs requires two tiers of adders and hence two delays. 15 inputs need 3 delays; all to establish the least significant bit.

Now if we suppose that the various pyramids are developed independently of each other, it will take say, 7 delays for the least significant bit of a 255 input counter, 6 for the next bit, 5 for the 3rd bit, and finally 1 delay for the 7th bit. Adding these delays together we have 28 delays required to do the counting. In general, if we have $2^n - 1$ inputs, we have $n - 1$ levels in the LSB pyramid and a total of

$$L_t = \frac{n(n - 1)}{2}$$

delays in generating the count. (See Table 7.1.)

TABLE 7.1

n	# of inputs	delay	Total delay
2	3	1	1
3	7	2	3
4	15	3	6
5	31	4	10
6	63	5	15
7	127	6	21
8	255	7	28
9	511	8	35

CARRY SHOWERS

A somewhat more intelligent way of generating the pyramids and of putting them together was suggested in 1971 (Foster, 1971). First, we establish a minimum number of delays. To get the least significant bit of the result requires at least $\lceil \log_3 N \rceil$ delays. Since the carry out of the final adder of each bit position must participate in the formation of the next more significant bit, and since there are $\lceil \log_2 (N + 1) \rceil$ bit positions, the theoretical minimum delay is $T_{min} \geq \lceil \log_3 N \rceil + \lceil \log_2 (N + 1) \rceil - 2$. The most significant bit is developed at the same time as the next most significant. The least significant bit was developed by the original pyramid. That accounts for the minus two in this equation.

Consider once again the pyramid that is used to generate the least significant bit of the output. Suppose that N is not a power of three. Then at some level in the pyramid we will have one or two outputs from the previous level leftover. We pass these leftover signals along to the next level and combine them if possible; if not, at the next level, or the next. Eventually, we will be down to three, two, or one signal remaining. If there is only one, we are through. If there are three, we need only one more full adder and we are through. If there are two signals, we can either use a half adder or else we can use a full adder and zero out the superfluous input line.

Now consider the second bit counter. After the first level of the least significant bit pyramid we will have some carry signals to work with. We shall begin to combine these as soon as they appear. These will in turn generate some carries of their own which we will process as early as possible, etc.

The reason for doing this is easy to understand. If we wait for the last carry from one bit to be established before we start work on the next bit, we will be cascading pyramids, each with its consequent delay. This was the method used by Favor. But if we begin processing as early as possible, we will have substantially reduced, with any luck, the number of signals left to be combined for bit i by the time we have finished processing bit $i - 1$. In Fig. 7.16 we show the process for $N = 31$.   Fig. 7.17 shows the circuit to realize this operation.

Consider the way in which Fig. 7.16 is constructed: 31 divided by 3 gives 10 and 1 left over. We put down 10 to the left and adding the 10 and the 1 write down 11 under the 31. This means that we will pass from the right-most column on the first level: 1) ten full adder *sum* signals and one *unprocessed* signal to the rightmost column, and 2) ten full adder carry signals to the column next to the left.

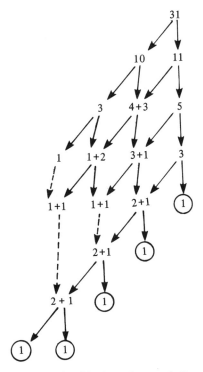

Fig. 7.16 Carry shower for $N = 31$. Dotted arrows indicate no processing.

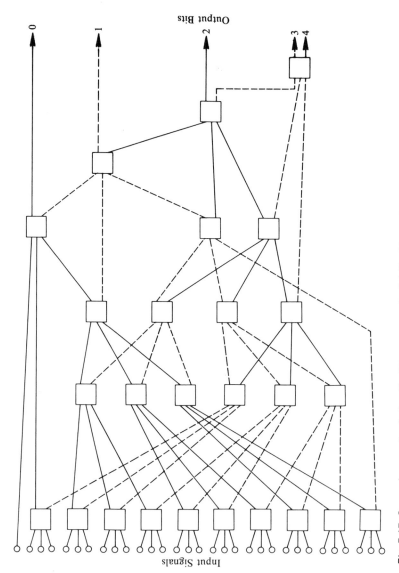

Fig. 7.17 Carry shower circuit for $N = 31$ constructed of full adders. Solid lines—signals contributing to even-numbered output bits; dotted lines—signals contributing to odd-numbered output bits.

On the second level, 11 divided by 3 gives 3 and 2 over. We write down 3 to the left and 3 + 2, or 5, under the 11. We can proceed in this fashion down the first column until we generate a one in that column. Now examine the second column. The 10 carry outputs we obtained from processing the original 31 inputs can be put into 3 full adders with 1 signal left over. So we write down three to the left (representing the carries) and four under the ten. The four we just wrote down must be combined with the three carries from the previous level of the column to the right. This gives seven, which in turn produces two carries and three signals to the next level in this column. The procedure continues in this fashion until all signals have been combined. Sometimes only one or two signals are available in a given column (see column four) for several levels. We will postpone combining these until we can utilize a full adder, or until it is obvious that no more signals will appear in this column because all columns to its right have terminated. To estimate the goodness of our lower bound, we wrote a computer program which proceeded in the manner of Fig. 7.16 to calculate the actual delays that would be found in a carry shower counter of the type described here. These delays were calculated for memory sizes of $2^n - 1$ with n ranging from 2 to 35. The values so obtained are shown in Table 7.2 together with the theoretical minimum delay. As may be seen, the actual values fall quite close to the predicted minimum, never exceeding it by more than 20 percent. The values do not behave smoothly with increasing n, although of course they do increase monotonically. This must be attributed to the natural "lumpiness" of integers.

Swartzlander (1973) has a further refinement on the above schemes. He presents a circuit very similar to a carry shower that has an easily calculable delay, and proposes this as an upper bound. (See Fig. 7.18).

To determine the delay time we argue as follows. Full adders 1, 2, 3, and 4 have their output ready after 1 unit delay. FA_6 and FA_8 are ready one unit later. FA_5 receives carry output from FA_6 (as does FA_7 from FA_8) and hence its output will be delayed one more unit, or three times. By similar arguments, it will take two more cycles to pass the signals through FA_{10} and FA_9 and in general two additional cycles for each additional level.

TABLE 7.2 COMPARISON OF THEORETICAL MINIMUM AND MAXIMUM NUMBER
OF DELAYS T WITH ACTUAL NUMBER OF DELAYS A FOR INCREAS-
ING NUMBER OF INPUTS N, GIVEN BY $2^n - 1$

n	T_{min}	A	T_{max}	n	T_{min}	A	T_{max}
1	0	0		19	29	35	35
2	1	1	1	20	31	36	37
3	3	3	3	21	33	37	39
4	5	5	5	22	34	39	41
5	7	7	7	23	36	41	43
6	8	9	9	24	38	43	45
7	10	10	11	25	39	45	47
8	12	12	13	26	41	47	49
9	13	14	15	27	43	49	51
10	15	16	17	28	44	51	53
11	16	18	19	29	46	53	55
12	18	20	21	30	47	55	57
13	20	23	23	31	49	57	59
14	21	25	25	32	51	59	61
15	23	27	27	33	52	61	63
16	25	29	29	34	54	63	65
17	26	31	31	35	56	65	67
18	28	33	33				

The network of Fig. 7.18 is made by taking two counters of size k inputs and, with a $\lceil \log_2 (k + 1) \rceil$ stage adder, making a $2k + 1$ input counter. If we call the delay in establishing the count of this circuit T_{max} we can add T_{max} to Table 7.2 and we see that A—the actual delay for a carry shower counter—is very close to T_{max}.

Next, Swartzlander suggests replacing the n stage adders (elements 5, 6, and 7, 8 and 9, 10, 11 of Fig. 7.17) by table look-up in a ROM. Operation is as follows. Concatenate the two inputs and the carry in to form an address. For example, $B_2 B_1 B_0 A_2 A_1 A_0 C_{in}$ will do for the adder 9, 10, 11. This 7-bit address will select one out of 128 words of the ROM which will contain 4 bits per word: Carryout, S_3, S_2, and S_1. Also replacing 5–6 by a ROM-fast adder and 7–8 by another we have the delay time Υ as

$$\Upsilon = \delta_{FA} + 2\delta_{ROM}.$$

This assumes that δ_{ROM} is independent of the size of the ROM, which is probably not the case. More likely, the access time of a ROM will be linearly related to the number of address bits required

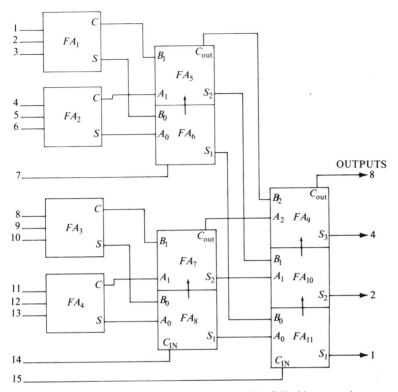

Fig. 7.18 Synthesis of a 15-input counter with a full-adder network.

to select a word. More important is the fact that such memories grow very large very fast and hence become an expensive solution to the problem.

PARALLEL INPUT AND OUTPUT

Another function that has been distributed over a memory is input and output (Foster, 1969). Suppose for simplicity we connect signals from the read heads of a 1024 track drum to the response store flip-flops of a 1024 cell CAPP. Now as a bit comes off each of the 1024 tracks in parallel, we write it into bit one of the memory. The next bit goes to bit two and so on. At one bit per microsecond, we are processing about one gigabit per second. That is a very respectable speed.

The operation can of course be reversed for copying from a CAPP to a drum.

SUMMARY

Given that associative memories have been around for fifteen years or so, it is rather surprising that the published literature contains so few papers on distributed hardware. The few that we could find are reviewed above.

8 | STARAN—NEW WAY OF THINKING

The STARAN computer designed and built by Goodyear Aerospace Corporation is the only computer designed around an associative memory that is currently for sale (Goodyear, 1972a; Goodyear, 1972b; Batcher, 1974; Davies, 1974; and Feldman, 1974). It is a complicated machine and many readers may wish to skip over the gory details that this chapter abounds in. On the other hand, given its unique position of being commercially available, it is incumbent upon any book about content addressable machines to present these details. We will first give an overview of the machine and then the details.

INTRODUCTION TO STARAN

No one could consider STARAN to be a cheap machine. Its initial price (since drastically reduced) was about half a million dollars for 256 words of associative memory with additional 256 word blocks available at around $4 per bit. And despite these somewhat luxuriant prices, a good part of the complexity of STARAN arises from attempts to lower the cost. One shudders at the possible price that would have resulted if straightforward brute force design techniques had been employed.

Add to this cost cutting a tendency to design op-codes with ever more complicated sub-sub-control fields and we get an architecture that the most generous hearted would label baroque and the small minded might call grotesque.

The three basic units of STARAN are the associative array, the controller unit, and the program memory. The controller fetches instructions one at a time from the program memory and executes them on the data stored in the associative array. The program memory is 32 bits wide and has an address space of 65 thousand words; about which more later.

The associative array consists of 1 to 32 blocks of memory that are 256 bits wide and 256 cells long. Each block has been made square and because of this the same hardware can be used to read out a word or a bit-slice.

The response store has three flip-flops per cell: M_i, X_i, and Y_i. Y is the tag bit and determines if the cell is or is not a responder. M is equivalent to the select bit of Chapter 5 and effectively determines whether or not cells respond to a command. X is a temporary storage bit used for various searches. Each instruction specifies what new value of X and Y will replace the old values as functions of old X, old Y, and F. This F typically is a bit slice read up from the cells of the block, but it may be a word stored in a special register called the "common register."

Input and Output operations may be conventional reads or writes from external devices or it may be via an optional parallel I/O channel that loads the response store in parallel from a fixed head disk or drum.

The program store of STARAN is not a simple one-layer store, as might be expected, but consists of a few page frames of high speed bipolar storage, some addresses reserved for direct memory access to a host computer and a fair amount of slow core storage. A "program pager" and a "sequential control unit" (a PDP-11) are provided to shuffle pages of instructions in and out of the high speed page frames. This is one of the more confusing aspects of the machine, but at the time STARAN was designed, bipolar storage was several times more expensive than core and it must have seemed good economics to design it in this fashion. Nowadays, I believe that with the lowered price differential, and the emphasis on straightforward architecture, the decision would have been made to go all the way with bipolar and hence eliminate a good deal of the complexity.

At this point, we are going to plunge into details and we will expect to rejoin the timid at the beginning of the next chapter.

OVERVIEW

Figure 8.1 shows an overview of the STARAN computer. There are six major blocks connected to each other and to the outside world. The parallel processor section is made up of three of these blocks: the AP Control Memory, the AP Control, and the Associative Array.

The Associative Array is of the type we have been discussing with distributed logic capabilities.   The Associative Processor control (APC) picks up instructions one at a time from the *APC* memory and issues them to the associative array.

The sequential control box is a PDP-11 which has its major responsibility communication with the operator and the monitoring of error conditions. The external function logic is the path by which the other elements communicate with each other.   The program pager is charged with the task of moving pages of AP control's pro-

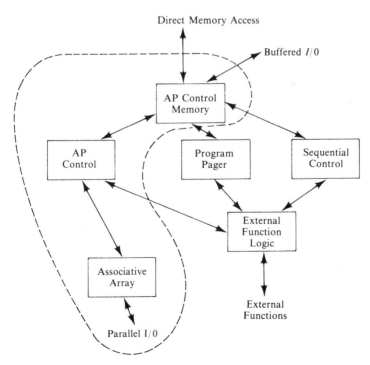

Fig. 8.1 Overview of the STARAN Computer.

grams from the slow parts of the APC memory into the fast parts when they are about to be executed. Several variations of input/ output are provided for. We will discuss them as we examine the respective elements of the machine.

ASSOCIATIVE PROCESSOR CONTROL (APC) MEMORY

Figure 8.2 and 8.3 show the APC memory in two different ways. All words are 32 bits long.

There are four blocks of 512 words made of bipolar semiconductors. The first three of these blocks (page 0, page 1, and page 2) are used to hold pages of instructions for AP control that are currently being executed. Paging is done on a request basis and with appropriate programming, the user can usually arrange to keep the about-to-

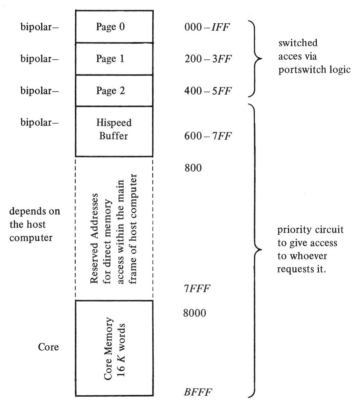

Fig. 8.2 Associative processor control memory.

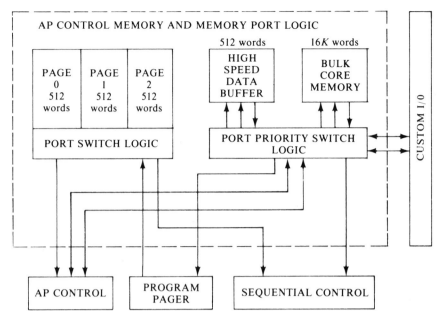

Fig. 8.3 AP control memory block diagram.

be-needed instructions in the high speed pages rather than in core. The high-speed-data-buffer (HSDB) is identical to the pages except that it can be used to store data as well as instructions and is accessible from the buffered I/O channel.

Addresses 800 hex through 7*FFF* hex are reserved for direct memory access. That means that if STARAN is attached to some host computer by adding certain amounts of circuitry, when STARAN references an address between these limits the data is plucked out of the host computer's main store. That way both machines—STARAN and the host—can access the same information and communicate with each other rapidly.

The remaining 16*K* words of APC memory are constructed from magnetic cores.

Access to pages 0, 1, and 2 is under control of three three-position switches called the "port switch logic." Each page can be connected either:

> The AP control *instruction bus*
> The Program pager
or   The sequential control

Changing the state of one or another of the switches is performed by the external function logic. For example, page 0 and page 2 might be connected to the AP control while page 1 was connected to the program pager. Attempts to reference a page to which you are not connected generates a "hang up" which halts your activity and interrupts the sequential controller (PDP-11) so it can take corrective action.

The high speed data buffer and the bulk core memory each have a scanner called the "port priority switch logic" that portions out accesses to them. First priority is given to the buffered I/O bus. If that bus does not desire an access then the AP control databus, the AP control instruction bus, the program pager bus, and the sequential control bus are examined in turn. The first one requesting access gets it and then the scan begins again from the top. Thus the sequential control bus gets into bulk core memory only if nobody else wants it. The two scanners (for the HSDB and the bulk core memory) operate independently.

If the direct memory access (DMA) to the host computer option is purchased a third scanner similar to the above is provided to control access to that storage.

RESERVED LOCATION

Certain locations in AP control memory are reserved for special purposes. In the bulk core memory these locations are:

> 8000   first AP control instruction taken from here
> 8001   AP control interrupt 1
>   .   .
>   .   .
>   .   .
> 800F AP control interrupt 15

When the AP control becomes active, the first instruction is taken from location 8000 without disturbing the APC program counter. If this instruction is a no-op the next instruction selected is controlled by the contents of the program counter and the APC takes up where it left off when it went inactive. If, one the other hand, the instruction in location 8000 is a branch, a new sequence is begun. Similarly, when interrupt N occurs, the next instruction is taken from location 800N. If it is a jump, the interrupt sequence is entered. If it is a no-op that interrupt is effectively disabled.

In the high speed data buffer, 8 locations (600 through 607 hex) are reserved for branch and link registers 0 through 7. These are used to facilitate subroutine linkages.

ASSOCIATIVE PROCESSOR CONTROL

The major purpose of the associative processor control is to control the associative processor. Instructions are drawn from the AP control memory and carried out on the associative array and on data stored in the APC control memory. Figure 8.4 shows the general layout of the AP control.

Under control of the program counter (in the program control box) an instruction is fetched from the APC memory and placed in

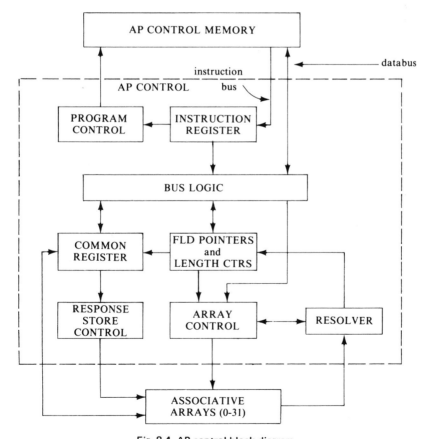

Fig. 8.4 AP control block diagram.

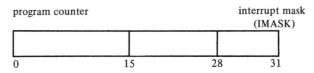

Fig. 8.5 The program status word.

the instruction register. Associated with the program counter in the program control box are the start and end loop markers and the comparator (See Fig. 8.5, 8.6, and 8.7). Upon execution of a "Loop β" instruction, stored in location α the address β is put into the end loop marker and $\alpha + 1$ into the start loop marker. The program counter (which points to the current instruction being executed) is continuously compared with contents of the end loop marker. When the two are equal, field length register $FL1$ is examined and if it is zero, exit from the loop to the next instruction at $\beta + 1$ takes place. If it is not zero, *one* is subtracted from the contents of $FL1$ and the

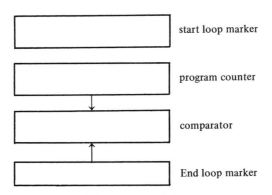

Fig. 8.6 Loop control elements.

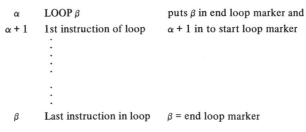

α	LOOP β	puts β in end loop marker and
$\alpha + 1$	1st instruction of loop	$\alpha + 1$ in to start loop marker
	.	
	.	
	.	
	.	
	.	
	.	
β	Last instruction in loop	β = end loop marker

Fig. 8.7 A loop written using the LOOP instruction.

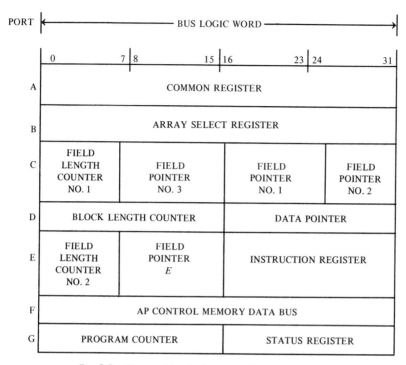

Fig. 8.8 AP control bus logic port and bit allocations.

contents of the start loop marker are placed into the program counter and the loop is repeated.

Data transmitted via the bus logic can be shifted left end around by 0, 8, 16, or 24 bits (0, 1, 2, or 3 bytes). The amount of the shift is specified by the instruction being executed.

A summary of the various registers is shown in Fig. 8.8. We will discuss them as we come to instructions which involve them.

A typical instruction not involving the associative array is a load register from memory. Briefly, this instruction loads a central register from associative processor control memory but with a staggering number of options. The instruction word consists of six fields:

bits 0–4—*op code* equal 00110—Load Register from Memory
      5–6—*operation*
              01   load lower half of register
              10   load upper half of register
              11   load both halves of register

7–9–*Group* specifies which register
    000–Common
    001–array select
    010–block length/data pointer
    011–program status word
    100–field length 2/field pointer E
    101–field pointer 2/field length 1
    110–field pointer 3/field pointer 1
    111–field length 1/field pointer 3/field pointer 1/field
        pointer 2.

10–11–left shift
    00 no left shift
    01 8 bits left end around
    10 16 bits left end around
    11 24 bits left end around

12–15–*Tag* specifies the way of computing the effective
address.
    0–undefined
    1–address
    2–address plus datapointer (DP)
    3–address plus DP, decrement block length (BL)
    4–address plus DP, increment DP
    5–address plus DP, decrement BL and increment
      DP
    6–address plus DP, decrement DP
    7–address plus DP, decrement BL and DP
    8–address + $R0$
    9–address + $R1$
    10–address + $R2$
    11–address + $R3$
    12–address + $R4$
    13–address + $R5$ $R0$–$R7$ are the branch and link
    14–address + $R6$ registers in the high speed data
    15–address + $R7$ buffer locations 600–607.

16–31–address.

Other variations on the Load Register from Memory exist:

Load Immediate–bits 16–31 of the instruction are used as data.

Store Register to Register–takes data from the source (S) register
and stores it in the destination register (D) with a left shift of 0, 1,
2, or 3 bytes.

Store Register to Memory—stores a register in a memory address. This instruction is the inverse of the "load register from memory" including all modes of addressing.

SWAP PSW—The present contents of the PSW (program status word) are stored in the effective address (EA) and the contents of the next memory word ($EA + 1$) are loaded into the PSW.

Some of the program control instructions include:

Conditional Branch

branch if condition met.

The conditions available for test include:

0—branch always—unconditional branch
1—branch never (a no-op)
2—if (FP1) = 0
3— (FP1) $\neq$ 0
4— (FP2) = 0
5— (FP2) $\neq$ 0
6— (FP3) = 0
7— (FP3) $\neq$ 0
8— (FL1) = 0
9— (FL1) $\neq$ 0
10— (FL2) = 0
11— (FL2) $\neq$ 0
} branch if FP1, FP2, FP3, FL1, or FL2 is zero or is non-zero.

12—bit of C register = 0
13—bit of C register $\neq$ 0
} selected by contents of FP1

14—no responders ($Y_i = 0$ for all i)
15—some responders ($Y_i = 1$ for some i)
16—(BL) = 0
17—(BL) $\neq$ 0
18—(FPE) = 0
19—(FPE) $\neq$ 0
20—(DP) = 0
21—(DP) $\neq$ 0

Addressing modes similar to load register from memory are available to modify the target address of the jump. Note that using an appropriate tag one can both test and decrement the Block Length register (BL) or the Data Pointer register (DP).

Branch and Link—This instruction stores the present program counter in the specified link register with zeros in the upper half, and then loads the effective address into the program counter.

Loop—repeat the instructions between $*+1$ and the effective address until the contents of FL1 go to zero. The contents of FL1 are decremented each pass and should initially contain the number of iterations minus one.

Load and Loop—repeat the instructions between $*+1$ and the address the number of times (plus one) specified in the loop count field of this instruction.

THE ASSOCIATIVE ARRAY

From one to 32 associative arrays may be connected to a STARAN. The Array Select Register has ones in bit positions 0 to 31 to indicate that arrays 0 to 31 are to participate in a search or response. Each array has 256 words of 256 bits each. Addressing may be in word mode or in bit-slice mode. A word may be divided into 8 fields of 32 bits each and read or written one field at a time from the Common Register. Associated with each word i there are three bits, the M_i, X_i, and Y_i bits, that form the three response store registers M, X, and Y. The X register is temporary fast storage and participates in logical operations as both source and destination along with the Y register and the bit of memory being queried. M is the mask register and determines which words of the array are to respond to a Store Operation. Y is *the* responder register that answers any search type operations.

Let us begin examining the array instructions with:

Load Response Store from Common—Copy the contents of the common register into one of the response store registers X or Y. The relevant sub fields are:

shift: shift the common register (padded with zeros in positions 32–255) right end around by 0, 1, . . . , 7 times 32 bits.

Logic one: if the bit of the common register pointed at by FP1 is one perform this logic function on the input and the destination. See below for description of the functions.

Logic Zero: if the bit of the common register is zero, do this logic function instead.

Change Y: do or do not change the Y response store. If we do change the Y register the ith bit of Y will become $(F_i \text{ op } Y_i)$ where F represents the contents of the common register.

Change X: we can specify: 1) do not change X 2) replace X_i by $(F_i$ op $X_i)$ or 3) replace X_i by $(F_i$ op $X_i)$ only where Y_i is one. Otherwise leave the old value of X_i: $(X_i \overline{Y_i} \lor Y_i(F_i$ op $X_i))$.

Mirror: reverse the bits of the input end for end (bit i becomes bit $256 - i$) before using it. (This does not actually change the input register. Just the quantity used for the calculation.)

The logic functions determined by Logic One and Logic Zero are (stated for Y and the input F):

0—Exclusive or with Complement of F, $Y \oplus \overline{F}$
1—Inclusive or with Complement of F, $Y \lor \overline{F}$
2—Logical and $Y \land F$
3—No-op Y
4—Load Complement of F $\overline{F}$
5—NOR $\overline{Y} \lor \overline{F}$
6—And Complement of F $Y \land \overline{F}$
7—Clear to zero 0
8—Load F F
9—Inclusive OR $Y \lor F$
10—NAND with Complement of F $\overline{Y} \lor F$
11—Set to one 1
12—Exclusive OR $Y \oplus F$
13—NOR with Complement of F $\overline{Y} \land F$
14—NAND $\overline{Y} \lor \overline{F}$
15—Negate $\overline{Y}$

Another instruction is:

Load Response Store Directly from Register—loads either X or Y from one of the response store registers X, Y, or M.

A field of the instruction allows one to select register X, Y, or M as the input data. Another option is "X or Y", which says: if all Y bits of an array are zero, X is the input source. Otherwise, Y is the source.

Load Response Store Direct from Array—uses a bit slice or a word from the array as an input.

Load Response Store Indirect from Array—as above except that field pointer FP1, FP2, or FP3 is used to select the bit slice or word. Some fields of this instruction are:

Pointer: specifies whether to use FP1, FP2, or FP3 to select the bit or word.

Modify Pointer: to the selected pointer, add one, subtract one, or do not change.

Change FP1: even if FP1 is not used to select the word or bit slice, it can be added to, or subtracted from, or not changed.

Change FPE: FPE may also be incremented or decremented or not changed. If both FP1 and FPE are changed, the direction of change must be the same.

Change length Counters:

Decrement FL1

Decrement FL2

Decrement BL

No Change

Load Response Store indirect through link pointer—registers FP1 and FP2 together constitute a link pointer which selects one array and one word from that array as source. This instruction changes the response store of only one array.

Store Response Store Register in Array—stores one of the response store registers (*X*, *Y*, or *M*) in a word or a bit-slice of the array. The address of the bit-slice or word may be specified directly or indirectly in FP1, FP2, or FP3. We may specify to use or not use a masked store. If the mask is specified, only those words or bit positions where the mask has ones will be modified. Those places where the mask has zeros will be left unchanged in the array.

In addition to the response store operations, shown above, there are options of these instructions which refer to the Mask Register.

The next group of instructions of interest refer to the Common Register:

Load Common Register—load a selected part of the Common Register from one array. FP1 specifies the array and FP2 the word or bit-slice to be used. All or part of the Common Register may be changed.

Store Common Register to Array—store all or part of the Common Register in an array word or bit-slice. Must be preceded by a Generate Mask to determine what portion of the Common Register will be stored.

Finally, there are the operations to select the first responder, etc.

Find First Responder—find the first bit in *Y* that is equal to 1. The array is entered into FP1 and the bit address into FP2.

Reset First Responder—clear the *Y* response store bit pointed at by FP1 and FP2.

Find and Reset First Responder—one instruction to do what the preceding pair did.

Reset Other Responders—leaves the first responder set and resets the *Y* bits of all other responders in the same array.

PROGRAM PAGER

The pager moves instructions from bulk core into the high-speed pages of memory. Activity is begun by an external function code (Load Get Register). Instructions are then taken sequentially from the locations pointed at by the Get Register until a Move data instruction is encountered.

The memory locations immediately following the Move data contain the data to be moved. The registers of the pager are:

GET Register—hold the address from which instructions for the pager and data to be moved are taken. GET is a self incrementing register.

PUT Register—holds the address to which data should be moved; usually within one of the three high-speed pages.

The instructions executable include:

EXF—external function asking the external function logic to assign a high-speed page to the program pager.

LOAD Put—copies bits 16–31 of the instruction into the Put Register.

MOVE DATA—begins a block transfer from the cells immediately following this instruction to the place pointed at by the PUT register. Bits 2–15 of this instruction specify how many words to move.

Load Put and Move Data—combination of the two preceding instructions.

Pager branch—copy bits 16–31 of this instruction into the GET register thus accomplishing an unconditional branch.

Pager Halt—Halt operation.

There are also Pager *Skip* and Pager *Halt* and *Skip* but the reason for these is not at all obvious.

EXTERNAL FUNCTION LOGIC

The external function logic is used to synchronize and coordinate the three independent parts of STARAN. The logic will poll the pager, the sequential processor and the associative processor control looking for a request. When a request is recognized, the polling stops. The request is honored and the sense information (see below) is returned to the requester. Then polling commences again. Thus, there can be no race conditions because the first request is completed and the results of that request provided to the world before any other request is serviced.

The external function logic allows the requester to specify certain conditions to be "sensed." If the desired test is "true" the external function logic increments the requesters program counter, causing the requester to skip its next instruction. For example, the AP control can say "skip if page 3 is connected to sequential control." One can also specify test and set in one instruction as we will see. The external function logic receives the low order 19 bits of each EXF instruction (bits 13–31). Some of the EXF instructions are:

Pager Port Switch—connect the specified page of high speed memory to the specified device. Fields of instruction are:

Page: which page are we concerned with?
Sense: skip* if one or more of the specified conditions is true:
page now connected to pager bus
page now connected to AP instruction bus
page now connected to sequential control
Set: a. If the page is currently connected to the pager bus connect it to X.
b. If the page is currently connected to the AP instruction bus, connect it to Y.
c. If the page is currently connected to the sequential bus, connect it to Z. (Where X, Y, and Z can independently specify the pager, AP instruction, or sequential bus.)

---

*Note that it is *not* the external function logic that is going to "skip." It is the device issuing the EXF command that will or won't skip.

This instruction then allows the program to specify the following sort of complex operation in one instruction:

"If page 3 is connected to the pager, don't change it and don't skip; but if it is currently connected to the AP instruction bus change it over to the pager bus and skip the next instruction. On the other hand, if this page is currently connected to the sequential bus, connect it to the AP instruction bus and don't skip the next instruction."

There are 64 "interlock flip-flops" in external function logic that the programmer may use in any fashion he sees fit. Interlocks $0-15_d$ are visible to and may be set by the operator. The other 48 are internal. The instruction that modifies an interlock flip-flop is:

Test and Set Interlock—has options which allow you to either:
  don't change interlock *n*
  Set interlock *n*
  Clear interlock *n*
  Complement interlock *n*
  Skip if interlock *n* is set
  Skip if interlock *n* is clear
  Skip if interlock *n* is set, then clear it
  Skip if interlock *n* is clear, then set it
  Skip if interlock *n* is set, and complement it in any event
  Skip if interlock *n* is clear and complement it in any event
  Skip if interlock *n* is set, in any case set it
  Skip if interlock *n* is clear, in any case clear it.

Other EXF instructions are:

Pager State—sense the state of the pager and then set it. Fields are:
  Test: skip if:
                pager is off (idle)
                pager is on (busy)
                don't skip
                always skip
  Set: turn the pager:
                on in any case
                off in any case
                don't change it
                complement its present state.

Pager Load Get Register—place bits 16–31 of this instruction into the pager GET register. If the pager was in operation that operation is aborted and a new operation is commenced. If the pager is off no action takes place and the Get Register is not changed.

Test and Set AP Interrupt—one of the 15 AP control interrupt conditions is tested and then set or cleared. Fields are:

    Which: specify which interrupt condition is to be examined.

    Skip: if interrupt is set, cleared, never, always.

    Set: clear the interrupt condition, set the condition, complement it, don't change it.

AP Activity—test and set the activity of the associative processor control. Fields to be specified are:

    skip: skip if AP is busy, idle, always, never.

    Set: make it active, make it idle, don't change it, complement it.

AP Loop Indicator—the AP loop indicator is set by the execution of a Loop or Load and Loop instruction by the AP control and is normally cleared by satisfying the loop count. Should an infinite loop be encountered, this instruction can be used to test and possibly clear the loop indicator. The fields are:

    skip: if AP control is in a loop, not in a loop, always, never.

    clear: do, or do not clear the loop indicator.

Error Control—test and set or clear one of the error conditions that may occur in the AP control. When such an error occurs the AP control is set inactive and an interrupt is issued to the sequential processor. Conditions include: illegal instruction, infinite loop, I/O bus hungup, AP data bus hung up, AP instruction bus hung up, Pager Get bus hung up, pager put bus hung up, and parity errors. Fields are:

    Error: specify which error condition is of concern.

    Skip: if condition is true, false, always, or never.

    Set: the new state of the error condition should be: off, on, the complement of what it was, the same as it was.

Sequential Interrupt—test and set or clear one of the eight interrupts from the external function logic to the sequential control. These interrupts have regular PDP-11 vector addresses to which the PDP-11 will transfer control on occurence of the interrupt. There are two such addresses with priority level 4, two with level 5 and two each with level 6 and 7. Fields are:

Which: give the identifier of the interrupt condition of concern.

Skip: skip next instruction if the interrupt condition is set, clear, skip in either event, don't skip.

Set: after deciding about the skip then set, clear; complement or don't change the condition.

INPUT/OUTPUT

STARAN has a variety of input/output options available. A custom I/O cabinet containing buffered and/or unbuffered I/O channels for data gathering, data receiving, and data storing devices may be obtained as part of the basic STARAN system. STARAN can also be integrated with a variety of other computer systems. A direct memory access (DMA) channel to a host-computer memory enables a rapid interchange of data between the systems in the common memory bank. A buffered I/O channel provides an alternate means of exchanging data, while an external function channel permits interrupts and/or other control information to be passed between the two systems.

An optional parallel input/output (PI/O) channel, with a width of up to 256 bits per array, can also be implemented in Staran *s*. The extreme width of this channel (up to 8,192 bits), plus its submicrosecond cycle time, gives Staran *s* an I/O bandwidth many times wider than that of a conventional computer. This PI/O channel can easily accommodate the high data rates that arise in many real-time applications. It is possible for Staran to connect with special high-bandwidth mass-storage devices, permitting rapid retrieval, restructuring, and processing of data in a large data base.

For instance, a head per track disc can be connected to the PI/O channel and with only one array 256 bits at a time can be ingested. At 0.3 microseconds per store, this gives 0.75 of a Gigabit per second bandwidth, which far exceeds any conventional input/output operations.

PROGRAMMING STARAN

For a programming example (Batcher, 1973) the basic loop of an unmasked add field's operation is selected. This operation adds the contents of a Field *A* of all memory words to the contents of a Field

B of the words and stores the sum in a Field S of the words. For n-bit fields, the operation executes the basic loop n times. During each execution of the loop, a bit-slice (a) of Field A is read from memory, a bit slice (b) of Field B is read, and a bit-slice (s) of Field S is written into memory. The operation starts at the least significant bits of the fields and steps through the fields to the most significant bits. At the beginning of each loop execution, the carry (c) from the previous bits is stored in Y and X.

$$x_i = c_i$$

$$y_i = c_i$$

The loop has four steps:

Step 1: Read Bit-slice a and exclusive-or ($\oplus$) it to X selectively and also to Y:

$$x_i \longleftarrow x_i \bar{y}_i \oplus y_i a_i$$

$$y_i \longleftarrow y_i \oplus a_i$$

The states of X and Y are now:

$$x_i = a_i c_i$$

$$y_i = a_i \oplus c_i$$

Step 2: Read Bit-slice b and exclusive-or it to X selectively and also to Y:

$$x_i \longleftarrow x_i \bar{y}_i \oplus y_i b_i$$

$$y_i \longleftarrow y_i \oplus b_i$$

Registers X and Y now contain the carry and sum bits:

$$x_i = a_i c_i \oplus a_i b_i \oplus b_i c_i = c_i'$$

$$y_i = a_i \oplus b_i \oplus c_i = s_i$$

Step 3: Write the sum bit from Y into bit-slice s:

$$s_i \longleftarrow y_i$$

Step 4: Read the X register and transmit it to both X and Y

$$x_i \longleftarrow x_i$$

$$y_i \longleftarrow x_i$$

This stores the carry bit into Y to prepare the registers for the next execution of the loop:

$$x_i = y_i = c_i'$$

Step 3 takes less than 250 nsec, while Steps 1, 2, and 4 each take less than 150 nsec. Hence, the time to execute the basic loop once is less than 700 nsec. If the field length is 32 bits, the add operation takes less than 22.4 microsec plus a small amount of setup time. The operation performs 256 additions in each array module. If four array modules are enabled, this amounts to 1024 additions to achieve a processing power of approximately 40 MIPS (million-instructions-per-second).

SUMMARY

STARAN is a complicated real life computer. Every attempt was made in its design to provide a machine that would execute rapidly most of the algorithms of Chapter 5. The best way to emphasize this for the reader to attempt to program any one of those algorithms (say, add fields) for STARAN. Then he will discover that the little baroque flourishes of the design have a real purpose behind them, and allow considerable speed-up of the algorithm.

The designers of STARAN will have their innings when they get to Chapter 10, where my best efforts are available for their criticisms.

9 | OTHER CONTENT ADDRESSABLE MACHINES

In addition to Staran several other machines have been proposed and/or constructed. In this chapter we will discuss a few of these and reference a lot of them.

A SECOND REAL MACHINE

Another content addressable machine was built by Goodyear Aerospace Corporation in 1965. It had no "name" but it was called the RADC 2048 word memory. (Goodyear, 1965a). RADC stands for Rome Air Development Center that funded the construction of the machine. Memory is a misnomer for this machine because although it was designed to be attached to a host computer (a CDC-1604B), it was functionally almost independent.

Figure 9.1 displays a general view of the registers of the machine. The 1604B external function could issue general commands to the AM to initiate and to sense for activity.

When the AM was activated by an external function instruction of the 1604B, the Program Counter would present an address to the Direct Memory Access (DMA) port on the 1604B and fetch a 48 bit word from the 1604B's core memory to load into the AM's instruction register. The DMA was designed to cycle-steal from the 1604B so that no CPU attention was required of the 1604B once it had

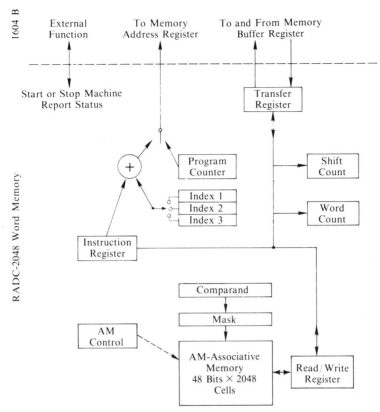

Fig. 9.1 General layout of the RADC-2048 word associative memory to direct memory access channel.

started the AM. Each instruction consisted of an opcode, two addresses, and some modifiers.

The Content Addressable Memory was built in two halves with each half sharing the response store logic with the other half. As in Fig. 9.2, there are two buffers (D and E) to hold the tag bits of the upper and lower halves, and one set of 1024 response store logic circuits. Searches and other operations are carried out first on the lower half of memory and then on the upper half. This was done to reduce the cost of the machine.

Consider the straightforward Exact Match of Comparand instruction (EMC). It had the following modifier fields:

1. *P* This tag allows the programmer to choose which of the halves of memory the instruction will operate on. Either

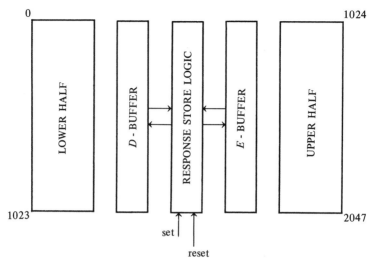

Fig. 9.2 The shared response store logic of the RADC memory.

half or both halves may be chosen. The lower half consists of words 0–1023, while the upper half consists of words 1024–2047.

2. *T* This tag allows the programmer to cause the buffers to shift activity forward one position (see Chapter 7) before execution of the operation. Since the buffers normally hold the previous results, the "advance buffer" allows searches to be extended over adjacent locations. Thus, this tag allows a measure of variable word length capability. Shift is from i into word $i+1$ with word 1023 shifting into word 1024 and word 2047 shifting into word 0.

3. *V* This tag allows the programmer to inhibit the initial manipulation of the response store for some operations. As applied to the EMC search, this means that the response store will not be initially set to all ones. Therefore the EMC search will be performed using only those locations whose response store elements were initially set. This allows the AND of many EMC searches to be performed using only the response store; this in turn allows the buffers to be used for a logical OR operation. Thus, this tag allows minterm-form Boolean algebra connections of EMC searches.

As applied to the Mismatch Comparand instruction (MMC), the tag will inhibit the response store from initially being re-

set to all zeros. This will allow the OR of MMC searches in
the response store saving the buffers for the AND. Thus, this
tag allows maxterm-form Boolean algebra connections of
MMC searches.

As applied to Load, and Unload, from 1604B, and Erase
operations operating on responders, this tag will inhibit the
initial transfer of results from the buffers into the response
store. This allows the programmer to transfer or erase data
as a function of the results of one search while preserving the
results of some other search in the buffers.

The value of the P tag will determine which of the two
possible sets of addresses is operated upon when V is a one.
Thus, an Erase First Responder 1, 0, 1 will erase the location
in the upper half of memory corresponding to the first response store element which is set. If the same element is set
but an EFR 0, 0, 1 is performed, the location effected will
have an address which is 1024 less than that of the first
example. If EFR 0, 0, 0 is specified, the first response stored
in the combined D and E buffers will be detected and that
location erased. Whatever was in the response store prior to
the operation is lost.

4. Z This tag allows the programmer to choose the connective desired at the end of a search. This connective is used to
specify how the previous results in the buffers will be effective by the new results in the response store. The first choice
is to replace the previous results with the new results (copy
both ONEs and ZEROs). The second is to store the logical
AND of the two results (copy ZEROs). The third offers the
OR connective (copy ONEs), while the fourth choice is to
leave the previous results uneffected.

5. Other instruction fields:

q_1—specifies one of the three index registers XR1, XR2 or XR3,
or else no indexing to be added to the mask address.

g—The effective address $G = g + (q_1)$ is used to fetch a mask
from 1604B memory to load into the mask register.

q_2—specifies an index register to be added to the comparand
address.

h—The effective address $H = h + (q_2)$ is used to fetch a comparand from the 1604B memory to load into the comparand
register.

LDR load AM registers (S, R, N) are used to put information into certain AM registers. The S field of the instruction goes to the shift count register. Shifting of the comparand is right, end-around. The R field goes into the AM address register and specifies an associative memory starting address at which some future action will take place. The N field goes to the word count register. For example, a Random Block Unload (RBU) instruction will transfer from the AM to the 1604B N words starting with the Rth word of the AM to the 1604B address specified in the RBU instruction.

The AM instructions include:

Between limiting comparands, Greater than or equal to, Greater than, Less than, Less than or equal to, Exact match, Mismatch to, Next higher than, Next lower than, Maximum and Minimum, as possible search operations.

Control instructions include:

Jump on no responders, Jump on index high, Jump on index low, and Jump unconditionally, and Store PC and jump. Load index, Increment index, Store index, Halt, Read first responder, Read address of first responder, Write in responder, and Write a block of words beginning with a fixed address or beginning with the first responder.

All in all, a reasonable set of instructions and much less rococo than the instruction set of Staran. This machine was delivered to Griffis Air Force Base (home of RADC) in 1966 and is still functioning.

A BRIEF MENTION

There are several other paper tigers with one or more interesting features. We will summarize a few of these here.

An organization of an Associative Cryogenic Computer by Robert Rosin (Rosin, 1962) is among the first papers to propose a stand-alone CAPP with instructions stored in the Content Addressable Memory. This machine has the ability to select the first responder but it does not permit communication between cells. Consequently, to find the "next instruction to be executed" is a bit clumsy. Each instruction has an "instruction bit" (B) set to one. Used (executed) instructions have an "instruction used bit" (IUB) set to zero while unexecuted instructions have an IUB of one. We then retrieve for the "first" word with $IB = 1$, $IUB = 1$ and clear the IUB to zero. This gives us the current instruction and sets up for reading the next one. Jumps are taken care of by retrieving the word with the correct "tag," (the same as that held in the jump instruction) and then setting all the IUB's below this point and clearing all the IUB's above this point. This is done using a chain bit or cascaded OR circuit that was described in Fig. 7.1.

Subroutines and interrupts have their own "used" bits and it is stated that subroutines can be nested but it is not clear exactly how this will happen.

Rosin recognizes the very important point that in a cryogenic machine (as in an all semiconductor machines) access to central registers is not *significantly* faster than access to main memory. There may be some difference—perhaps a factor of two—but it is far, far less than the ratio of vacuum tube or transistor flip-flops to core speeds. His machine design takes account of this fact by reducing the number and usage of control registers.

Albert Kaplan (Kaplan 1963) proposed an add-on memory—72 bits per word—4096 words. Thirty-six bits are content addressable and 36 are conventional memory. The interesting aspect of Kaplan's machine is that it has the capability of counting the number of responders. Using a resistive summing network and an analog to digital converter (see Fig. 9.3), he is able to get an approximate (± 10%) count of the number of responders in 24 microseconds.

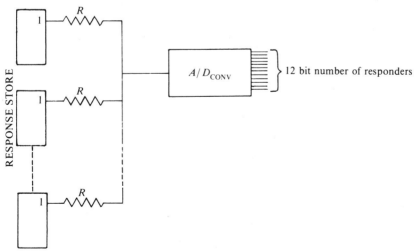

Fig. 9.3 Kaplan's approximate number of responders circuit.

Using the response store as a ten-megahertz shift register and employing a counter, he is able to get an exact count of the number of responders in 410 μsecs.

C. Y. Lee (Lee 1962) presents the very first combination of content addressability with intercell communication. His cells are eight bits long and hold one character. "Active" cells which meet search criteria can transfer their activity to successor or predecessor cells (right hand or left hand neighbors). A search might go as follows: all cells become active. Cells containing the letter N transfer activity right (all others reset). Active cells containing the letter O transfer right. Active cells containing W transfer right. We follow with selections for: blank, I, S, blank, T, H, E, blank, T, I, M, E, blank, F, O, R, etc.

Thus we can narrow down to the correct string in storage very rapidly, independent of the overall size of the memory. Read out of active cells is provided but little is said about the controlling device, the problem of multiple responders, or how to tell if there are *any* responders.

Seeber (1960) in an early article described a memory capable of sorting input words as they arise. Comparators at each word tell if the next input is greater than, equal to or less than the word stored at that cell.

Since words are kept sorted in ascending order, when a new word is presented the last 29 words, for example, will all show "greater than comparand." Words greater than the comparand move down one space leaving a gap. The new word is then entered into this gap and we are ready to start again. Note that this article was written before the "minimum" search algorithm was published. Since that time such a cumbersome and expensive memory has been obsolete. We merely search for the minimum, read it out, erase it, and start again. There is no need to *keep* the words in order, only to *retrieve* them in order.

N. Natarajan and P. Thomas (Natarajan, 1969) propose two complete sets of interrogation hardware complete with two separate response stores. Then an AM could be used by two processors with true simultaneity. R. Ewing and P. Davis (Ewing, 1964) discuss a machine that looks a great deal like Staran in its registers and in its horizontally microprogrammed instruction word.

In 1970 the present author designed a machine that has one or two interesting features (Foster, 1970B). SAM is a self contained

CAPP with instructions stored in the AM. There is an *instruction* register, a *comparand* register, a *mask* register and 64 coordinate addressed scratch pad locations. These are used to hold results and also comparands and masks. AM words contain eight bytes and five response store bits: $T_1 T_2 T_3 T_4$ and I.

The basic instruction cycle has three phases:

1. Find the first responder on I and copy its contents into the IR.
2. Move the activity on I forward one position.
3. Execute the instruction in the IR.

Instructions must be stored in the order that they are to be executed with no intervening data. Unconditional jumps have the format "JMP name" and cause a search for a word containing "NOP name." The search is carried out on the I bit. Conditional tests are all in the form of "skip if ... " which skips the next instruction (advances activity on I one extra place) if the condition is met.

Tag bits ($T_0 T_1 T_2$ and T_3) can be set, complemented, anded and ored together, moved forward or backward and the first responder can be saved (all others reset) or discarded (all others unchanged).

Searches and multiwrites are done using a particular tag bit. For example, the instruction WIN 3, 26, 19 will "winnow" (discard the chaff and keep the wheat) on tag bit 3 using the contents of register 26 as a mask and the contents of register 19 as a comparand.

Subroutine jumps are shown in Fig. 9.4. The ENR 60 instruction puts the next word (USK SMITH) into register 60. JMP JONES transfers control to the beginning of the subroutine. Finally, RJP 60

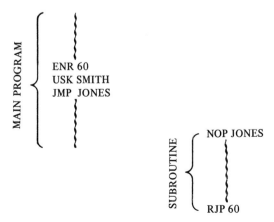

Fig. 9.4 Subroutine jumps and returns in SAM.

causes a search (on I) for a cell containing a word which matches the contents of register 60. When the USK SMITH is found and executed it causes an unconditional skip *over* the jump to JONES and the main program continues. SMITH is merely a label used to identidy this particular return location.

Although this subroutine calling procedure is clumsy, in a machine lacking coordinate addressing capability there are only a few ways of carrying this out. The problem is that AM's are essentially unstructured spatially whereas programs have an inherent order: a beginning, a middle and an end. Were there any such animal as a really nonprocedural language which stated eternal verities about the universe then an AM would be the place for that language.

David Digby (1973) shows a method of testing many comparands against the memory simultaneously. I was particularly interested in this since I had proven it impossible to achieve as early as 1964. (Foster, 1965). Like the bumble bee, Mr. Digby was unaware of my impeccable logic and went ahead to devise the following algorithm.

For the sake of argument, let us suppose that there are 17 comparands we wish to test against the memory to see if any of them are present (exact match). Such a problem might arise when we wish to find the set of items common to two separate lists, to find the intersection of the lists.

We reserve 17 bits in each word to hold match or mismatch with the 17 comparands. Initially, these bits ($C1$–$C17$) are all *one*. The algorithm works bit serially. We examine the Nth bit of each of the comparands and find those that have a *zero* as their N^{th} bits. Suppose it was comparands 1, 3, 12, and 17. Then we select those memory words that have a *one* in their N^{th} bits and write *zero* (mismatch) in their bits $C1$, $C3$, $C12$, and $C17$. We then select the memory words that have a zero in the Nth bit and since the remaining comparands have *one* in this bit position we write *zero* (mismatch) in the bits $C2$, $C4$–$C11$, and $C13$–$C16$. If we wish to allow some of the comparands to have $\emptyset$ (don't care) in a given bit position, we just have to take care of the comparands with *zero* and the comparands with *one* and ignore the comparands with $\emptyset$.

For example, suppose in some particular bit position, comparands 1–5 have *zeros*, comparands 6–10 have *ones*, and comparands 11–17 have *don't cares*. We select all the memory cells with *zero* in this bit position. These clearly don't match comparands 6 through 10, so we write *zeros* in bits $C6-C10$. Next we select those cells in memory with *ones* in this bit position. These just as clearly don't match comparands 1-5 so we write *zeros* in their $C1-C5$ bits. We do nothing to cell bits $C11-C17$ on this pass because these comparands don't care what the words hold and hence no mismatches are possible. By writing *zero* in a C bit whenever a cell disagrees with that comparand, we end up with only those cells that agree everywhere still having a *one* in that C bit.

The reader should note that the search time (but not the cell space used up) is independent of the number of comparands compared; providing of course, there is appropriate central hardware to generate the sets of "comparands that require *zero*/*one* in this bit position," and provided that multiple bit writes are possible.

Given K comparands with B bits each, successive matches would require $K \cdot B$ probes of a regular CAPP memory whereas Digby's needs only $2B$.

In order to present the comparands to the data array in the fashion required for this algorithm we need a small memory with access in two perpendicular directions (see Fig. 9.5). Several papers have reported schemes for accomplishing this "orthogonal" accessibility.

Digby also characterizes the kinds of search operations it is possible to do in a CAPP. Consider a bit serial operation. In each bit position that is going to be investigated, we have the possibility that the com-

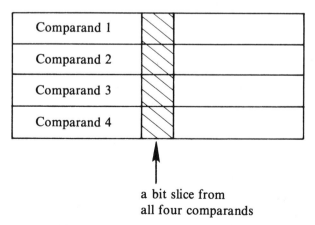

a bit slice from
all four comparands

Fig. 9.5 A bit slice of four comparands for use in Digby's Many-to-Many comparison scheme.

parand is *zero* or *one* and the possibility that the word(s) in memory are *zero* or *one*. This gives four possibilities:

Comparand,	Word
0	0
0	1
1	0
1	1

Add to this the initial (upon entry to the operation) thing that is done to the tag bit (set, or clear, or leave alone) and we have a quintuple. In each position of the quintuple, we can choose to make the tag bit *zero* "0," make it *one* "1," or do Nothing "*N*."

Thus, for example in the exact match operation we have:

condition: Start 00 01 10 11
operation: 1   *N*   0   0   *N*

We initialize the bit to *one* and then clear it to *zero* when we find a mismatch, but leave it alone (do nothing) if the comparand bit and the word bit agree. Then by the end of the search, over many bits, only those words which exactly match the comparand in every searched bit will have a tag of one.

There are five opportunities to make a choice between three things to do ("0," "1," "*N*") so there are $3^5 = 243$ possible searches. Not all of these represent valid searches, however, since the following is true:

1. There must be at least some 1 or 0 among the five values, or else no search will occur.
2. If the START value is 1 or 0 then at least one of the other cases must have the opposite value, or else the initial value will remain unchanged.
3. If the search is to cover more than one bit position, then there must be at least one *N* among the values (other than START). Otherwise, the last bit examined will erase any contribution made by earlier bits.

After eliminating the 79 possibilities that violate one or more of these restrictions, there remain 164 actual search possibilities. These may be divided into two categories, according to whether or not the

TABLE 9.1 ARITHMETIC SEARCH PRESCRIPTION

Start Value	Values for cases 00	01	10	11	Description of corresponding search on C and D (arithmetic relation required for result = ONE)
1) 0	N	0	1	N	Data less than comparand (positive numbers)
2) 1	N	0	1	N	Data less than or equal to comparand
3) N	N	0	1	N	(Same as 2 above, except equal case determined by results of previous search)*
4) 0	N	1	0	N	Data greater than comparand (positive numbers)
5) 1	N	1	0	N	Data greater than or equal to comparand
6) N	N	1	0	N	(Same as 5 above, except equal case determined by results of previous search)*
7) 0	0	N	N	1	Carry-out from sum of data and comparand
8) N	0	N	N	1	(Same, but including carry-in from previous)
9) 1	N	0	0	1	Highest ONE bits match (includes all-ZERO case)
10) 0	N	0	0	1	Highest ONE bits match (but *not* all-ZERO case)

*For two's complement numbers, use No. 6 search on sign bit after No. 1 or No. 2 search, or No. 3 on sign bit after No. 4 or No. 5 search.

search results are sensitive to the sequential order in which the bits are examined, as follows:

1. The bit sequence is significant if there are both 1's and 0's among the prescription values (other than START). This is the equivalent to carry propagation in an adder, and this category will therefore be referred to as "arithmetic." There are 108 prescriptions in this category, but only a few have a clearly recognizable arithmetic meaning. These are listed in Table 9.1.

2. The bit sequence is *not* significant if there are only 1's or only 0's among the prescription values (other than START). The 56 prescriptions in this category will be referred to as "logical." Thirty-two of these deal with fixed constants in one or both words, and the remaining 24 are listed in Table 9.2.

Some caution is warranted in accepting these results at face value. There is interaction between the bits that is not completely accounted for in Table 9.1. For instance, consider search 4 which purports to be a search for "greater than the comparand." According to Digby, we begin at the left hand end of the word with the tag bit *zero* and if the data bit and comparand bit agree we do nothing. If the comparand is zero and the data word is one we know that the comparand is less than the data, whereas if the comparand is *zero*

TABLE 9.2   LOGICAL SEARCH PRESCRIPTION

	Start Value	Values for cases 00	01	10	11	Description of corresponding search on C and D (Set-function required for result = ONE)
1)	1	N	0	0	N	Exact match ($C = D$)
2)	N	N	0	0	N	(Same, except AND'd with previous search)
3)	0	1	N	N	1	Some bit matches ($C \neq \overline{D}$)
4)	N	1	N	N	1	(Same, except OR'd with previous search)
5)	1	0	N	N	0	Exact complements ($C = \overline{D}$)
6)	N	0	N	N	0	(Same, except AND'd with previous search)
7)	0	N	1	1	N	Mis-match ($C \neq D$)
8)	N	N	1	1	N	(Same, except OR'd with previous search)
9)	0	N	N	N	1	Intersection ($C \cap D \neq$ "all ZERO's")
10)	N	N	N	N	1	(Same, except OR'd with previous search)
11)	1	N	N	N	0	Non-intersection ($C \cap D =$ "all ZERO's")
12)	N	N	N	N	0	(Same, except AND'd with previous search)
13)	0	N	N	1	N	C not subset of D ($C \cap D \neq C$)
14)	N	N	N	1	N	(Same, except OR'd with previous search)
15)	1	N	N	0	N	C is subset of D ($C \cap D = C$)
16)	N	N	N	0	N	(Same, except AND'd with previous search)
17)	0	N	1	N	N	D not subset of C ($C \cap D \neq D$)
18)	N	N	1	N	N	(Same, except OR'd with previous search)
19)	1	N	0	N	N	D is subset of C ($C \cap D = D$)
20)	N	N	0	N	N	(Same, except AND'd with previous search)
21)	0	1	N	N	N	Incomplete union ($C \cup D \neq$ "all ONE's")
22)	N	1	N	N	N	(Same, except OR'd with previous search)
23)	1	0	N	N	N	Complete union ($C \cup D =$ "all ONE's")
24)	N	0	N	N	N	(Same, except AND'd with previous search)

and the data *one* we know that the comparand is greater than the data. Digby says to write *one* in the first case and *zero* in the second. But if the search is to be performed properly, this must be done only *once*: in the most significant bit at which a disagreement is found. What is needed is a bit in the word saying "still undecided" and only data words in that condition should receive further processing.

But this involves two bits of the data word, the not-processed bit and the bit under consideration, both of which must be examined and changed simultaneously. Digby does not consider this more complicated problem, and no wonder, with three things to do to each bit and three bits to consider (two in the data word and one in the comparand), we have 9^9 or 3^{18} (about 370 million) prescriptions to consider. It is unfortunate that many of the more interesting algorithms fall into this latter category.

Next we shall look at a hardware technique proposed originally by Lewin (1962) and later discussed by Wolinsky (1968) and by Ahrons (1963).

What Lewin proposed was a two-rail readout system. There would be two wires for each bit position, and if a responder stored a *zero* in this position, it would activate the "zero" line. If another responder stored a *one* it would activate the "one" line. If all responders stored *zeros*, only the "zero" line would be active. If some responders stored *zero* and some store *one*, then both lines will be active; what Lewin calls a "mixed" state and symbolizes by X. Suppose we wish to retrieve items in increasing order: select all candidates; look at the leftmost bit position that is displaying an X (some responders have *zero* here and others have *one*). Discard all words which have *one* stored here (select for *zero* in this position). Now we have a smaller group of responders to work with. Again select the leftmost X and require it to be *zero*. Repeat until there are no more X's. Then read out the only word that is still a responder (we assume no duplicates). Now go back to the most recent bit position where there was an X that you made zero. Now select for that position to be *one*. Read out that word. Repeat this backtracking. Each time you change a *zero* specification into a *one* specification, make all bit positions to the right of this one into "don't cares" as far as selection is concerned.

Obviously, this procedure repeated often enough will retrieve all the words in increasing order. What Lewin then shows is that if there are m words to be retrieved, his algorithm takes *exactly* $2m - 1$ probes of memory to get them all.

The proof is by induction. Suppose it does take $2m - 1$ probes to retrieve in order m words. Consider what you are doing when you "require a zero" in the left-most bit position that displayed an X. You are breaking the set of responders into two parts. One part that has *zero* here that you are keeping and the other part that has *one* here that you are temporarily putting to one side to be investigated later. Suppose the part you are keeping has k responders and the other part therefore has $m - k$ members. It took you one probe of memory to do the division into parts and if our hypothesis is correct, it will take you $2k - 1$ probes to do the zero part and $2(m - k) - 1$ probes to do the one part. Adding these up we have

$$1 + (2k - 1) + (2(m - k) - 1) = 2m - 1$$

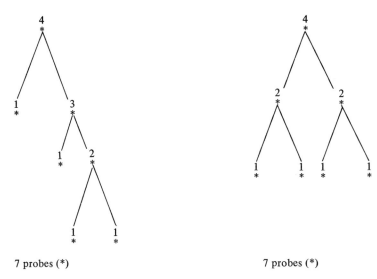

7 probes (*)   7 probes (*)

Fig. 9.6 Two possible cases of Lewin's method of dividing four words for ordered retrieval.

which shows that if it is true for m it is true for $m + 1$. Figure 9.6 shows the two possible ways that four words can be split up at the end of one of the partitionings. Since our conjecture is true for 1, 2, 3, and 4 words in a partition and we know that if it is true for n it is true for $n + 1$, then we have proved what Mr. Lewin asserted.

It would seem that by the time we got down to a pair of words and split them we would know their patterns and not have to probe to read them out. But they may differ in several bit positions and we don't know until we probe who has the *zeros* and who has the *ones* belonging to the unresolved X's.

ADDENDUM

Many other designs have been proposed. Among the more interesting ones are papers by Berg (1972), Feng (1968), Fuller (1965a, 1967), Kautz (1969) Lipovski (1969), McKeever (1965), Slotnick (1967), and Urban (1972). For complete listings of papers in the field, see either of the two large bibliographies by Parhami (1973) and Minker (1971).

Several unconventional devices have been used (on paper at least) to realize CAPP's. Crofut (1966) proposes a delay line memory while Rux (1969) would make the line out of glass. Harding (1968) has a $2\frac{1}{2}$ D memory while Stone (1968) would make a modified memory for a general purpose machine. Finally, Gabor (1969) and Sakaguchi (1970) propose the use of holography to attain content addressability.

SUMMARY

We have looked at several machines that have been built or proposed as CAPP's. We have not begun to attempt to look at all the ones there are, but rather have selected a few with interesting or original features that seemed worthy of discussion.

10 | AN EMBODIMENT

In this chapter we are going to try to summarize what we have learned in the rest of the book and come up with a physical embodiment of an ideal CAPP. In particular, we will try to fit this into what we know about semi conductor technology. That can be summed up in just a few words: "48 pins per chip is possible; 200 pins per chip is expensive. You can just about get 4000 bits of storage on one chip in 1975."

There are three aspects to the design: the Content Addressable Word itself, the interconnection logic, and the central control unit. We will discuss them in turn.

THE CONTENT ADDRESSABLE WORD

Figures 10.1 through 10.5 show the design of a single bit serial content addressable word. It consists of 64 bits of memory, three response store flip-flops (R, S, and T), and has been designed to require only 20 active pins. Adding in at least two pins for power supply, this is still under 24 pins, which is a standard configuration for a DIP chip. DIP stands for "dual in line pins" and is a common method of packaging integrated circuits.

The command decoder (Fig. 10.1) is an almost exact copy of a type "9311 one of sixteen decoder" that is commercially available

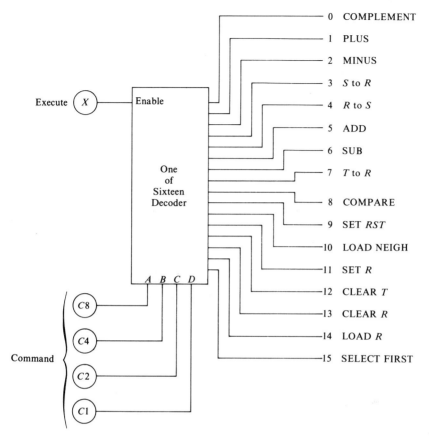

Fig. 10.1 The content addressable word Command Decoder.

from a number of sources. It accepts a four bit command and upon presentation of an execute signal, energizes one of sixteen output lines. These lines are labelled to help the reader discover their intent.

Figure 10.2 shows the memory. This consists of a 64 bit read-write random access memory similar to but smaller than a 93410 256 bit RAM. W and $\overline{W}$ are the value and the complement of the bit of the word being addressed. A six bit data address selects one of the 64 bits and if the R flip-flop is set, presents the value of the bit (W) at OUT. The value on the data line is written into the selected memory bit when the write line is energized. Data is *one* if R is *one* and C (the broadcast value of the comparand bit) is energized, or if $\overline{R}$ is *one* (R is *zero*) and C is not energized. Writing can be done only into

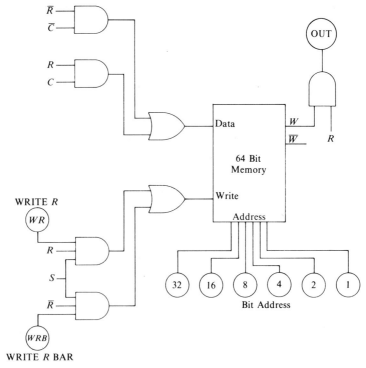

Fig. 10.2 The content addressable word Memory.

those cells with S equal to *one*. If R is *one* and we energize WRITER or if R is *zero* and we energize WRITERBAR we try to write into the selected bit of the memory. This gives us a number of options:

where S is *one:*

—write *one* in responders. Do not change non-responders. Energize C and WRITER.

—write *one* in non-responders. Do not change responders. Energize WRITERBAR and $\overline{C}$.

—Write *zero* in responders. Do not change non-responders. Energize WRITER.

—Write *zero* in non-responders. Do not change responders. Energize WRITERBAR.

—Store R in all cells. Energize WRITER, WRITERBAR and C.

—Store $\overline{R}$ in all cells. Energize WRITER, WRITERBAR and $\overline{C}$.

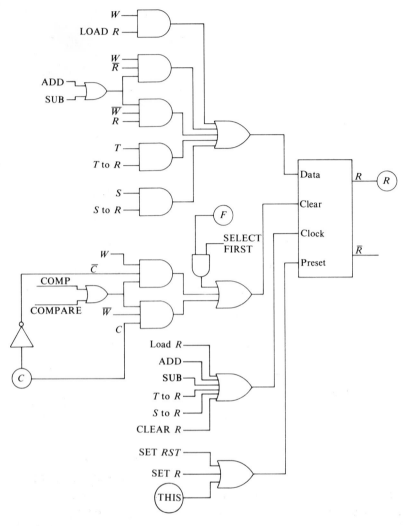

Fig. 10.3 *R* flip-flop.

The *R* and *T* flip-flops are standard *D*-type flip-flops roughly equivalent to half a 7474 with data, clock, preset and clear inputs and both *Q* and *Q̄* outputs available. *Clear* makes *Q* false and *Q̄* true while *preset* does the opposite. They work at any time independent of the clock. When the clock goes from *zero* to *one* the value at *data* is copied into the flip-flop. The *S* flip-flop is a somewhat simpler "*RS*-

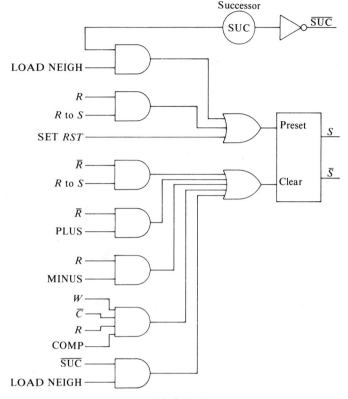

Fig. 10.4 *S* flip-flop.

type" without a clock. It simply remembers which input (preset or clear) was most recently *one*. (See any standard text on electronics.)

Perhaps the easiest way to explain the circuits of Fig. 10.1 to 10.5 is to discuss the eight algorithms they are intended to carry out efficiently.   Reference should be made to Chapter 5 in case of difficulty although there are some differences between that chapter and this.

Exact match
   initial conditions: *SET R*
   repeat for all *i*:
      bit address (*i*), C_i, *Compare, execute.*
   final: *R* is set for exact match. Reset elsewhere.

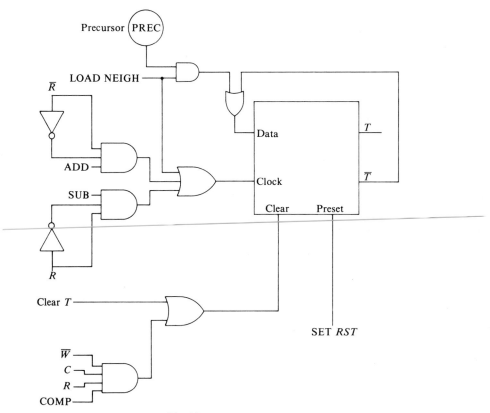

Fig. 10.5 *T* flip-flop.

General Compare
    initial conditions: *SET RST*
    repeat for all *i*:
        bit address (*i*), C_i, *COMP, execute.*
    final: $R = 1$ equals, $S = 1$ less than, $T = 1$ greater than comparand.
Maximum
    initial conditions: *SET RST*
    repeat for all *i*:
    1. *bit address* (*i*), $C_i = 1$, *Compare, execute*
    2a. if SOME · *R: PLUS, execute*—this clears *S* where *R* is *zero*
    2b. if NO · *R: S to R, execute*—copy *S* to *R*
    final: $R = 1$ for largest cell of array.

Minimum
    initial conditions: *SET RST*
    repeat for all i:
       1.   *bit address (i), $C_i = 0$, Compare, execute*
       2a. if SOME $\cdot$ *R: PLUS, execute*
       2b. if NO $\cdot$ *R: S to R, execute*
    final: $R = 1$ for smallest cell of the array.

Add One
    initial conditions: *SET RST*
    repeat:
       1. *bit address, Load R, execute*
       2. *WRITER, WRITERBAR, C = 0*   store $\overline{R}$
       3. *PLUS, execute*   copy 0 from R to S

Subtact One
    initial conditions: *SET RST*
    repeat:
       1. *bit address, Load R, execute.*
       2. *WRITER, WRITERBAR, C = 0*
       3. *MINUS, execute*

Add fields $(A + B \rightarrow A)$
    initial conditions: Clear R, execute
                           Clear T, execute
    repeat:
       1. *bit address of A, ADD, execute*
       2. *bit address of B, ADD, execute*
       3. *WRITER, WRITERBAR, C = 1, bit address of A*
       4. *T to R, execute*
       5. *Clear T,* execute

Subtract Fields $(A - B \rightarrow A)$
    initial conditions: *Clear R execute*
                           Clear T execute
    repeat:
       1. *bit address of A, ADD, execute*
       2. *bit address of B, SUB, execute*
       3. *WRITER, WRITERBAR, C = 1, bit address of A*
       4. *T to R, execute*

It appears strange that subtraction should take one less step than addition, but Table 10.1 shows why with this particular hardware configuration this is so. To add we must clear T. To subtract we must not.

TABLE 10.1   ADD/SUBTRACT FIELDS.

debit or carry	A	B	ADD initial T	R	ADD final T	R	SUBTRACT initial T	R	SUBTRACT final T	R
0	0	0	0	0	0	0	0	0	0	0
0	0	1	0	0	0	1	0	0	1	1
0	1	0	0	0	0	1	0	0	0	1
0	1	1	0	0	1	0	0	0	0	0
1	0	0	0	1	0	1	1	1	1	1
1	0	1	0	1	1	0	1	1	1	0
1	1	0	0	1	1	0	1	1	0	0
1	1	1	0	1	1	1	1	1	1	1

TABLE 10.2   TIMES IN MICROSECONDS FOR THE ALGORITHMS TO EXECUTE A 16-BIT FIELD ASSUMING A 100 NANOSECOND CYCLE TIME.

Exact Match	1.7
Compare	1.7
Maximum	4.3*
Minimum	4.3*
Add One	4.9
Subtract One	4.9
Add fields	8.0
Subtact Fields	6.5

*Including 1 μsec for 16 determinations of SOME or NO responders.

Table 10.2 shows the times required to execute these 8 algorithms for a 16 bit field. We have assumed that each step requires 100 nanoseconds. This is probably conservative, but not drastically so.

These algorithms exercise most of the commands that can be broadcast to the cells. The exceptions are *R to S, LOAD NEIGH*, and *SELECT FIRST*. The necessity of select first we have discussed before. *R to S* is provided to give an ability to load *S*. *Load neighbors* copies the precursor to *T* and the successor to *S*.

THE INTERCONNECTION LOGIC

There are three functions that must be performed by the interconnection logic. These are "move activity," "select first," and "address." The former is a simple matter of hooking up each cell

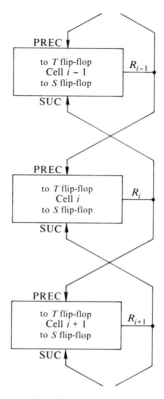

Fig. 10.6 The connections for moving activity forward and back.

with its neighbors (see Fig. 10.6). The R output of each cell goes to the "Prec" input of its successor and to the "Suc" input of its precursor. On the command "LOAD NEIGH" the S flip-flop of each cell is set to the same state as the R flip-flop of its successor and the T flip-flop to the same state as the R flip-flop of its precursor.

Then by copying S to R or T to R we accomplish "move activity backward" or "move activity forward," respectively, as we may desire. This provides us with a one dimensional ordering of the cells of memory. This will allow us to have data words that exceed 64 bits in length. It seems a reasonable compromise between no cell interconnections and a two dimensional grid.

The "select first" logic is shown in Fig. 10.7 and 10.8. We have chosen to design the blocks with eight inputs (see the discussion in chapter 7). This requires a maximum fan in of eight; it requires

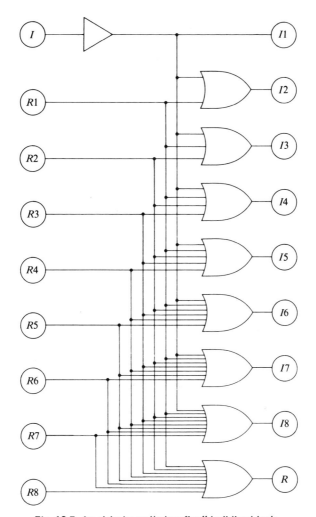

Fig. 10.7 An eight-input "select first" building block.

eight gates and an inverter. Using 7400 type logic, the gate delay
is the order of 15 nanoseconds per gate. In the tree of Fig. 10.8,
there are 4 levels with 512 blocks on the first level, 64 on the second,
8 on the third, and one on the fourth level for a total of 585 blocks.
Propagating a signal from cell 0 to cell 4095 we pass through four
gates to reach the SOMER line for a delay of 60 nanoseconds. The
select first signal passes through three gates on the way up, one
gate to cross the top block and two gates per block, or six gates on

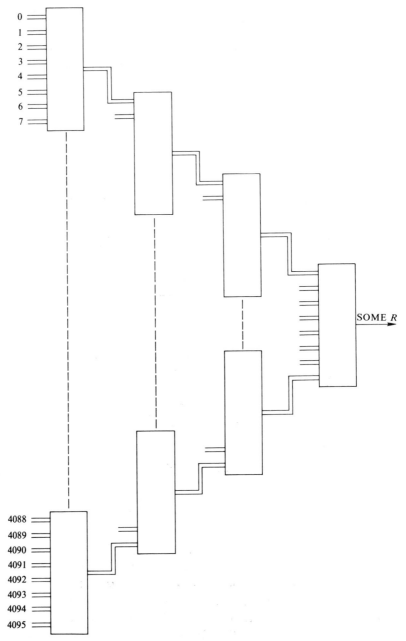

Fig. 10.8 The select first tree for eight-input blocks; 4096 cells.

the way down.   This is a total of 10 gates or 150 nanoseconds to select the first responder.

Even in a CAPP we would like to be able to reference words by an address. Of course, one way to accomplish this is to set aside 12 bits in each word and store there a unique number between 0 and 4095. To accomplish this more economically, we use a dual access switching tree as shown in Fig. 10.9. The main square consists of the intersection of 64 horizontal and 64 vertical lines. At each intersection there is a two input AND circuit whose output goes off to connect to the THIS input of a cell of the CAPP. The 64 horizontal (and vertical) lines are in turn driven by AND circuits at the intersection of an 8 X 8 grid. The inputs to the squares of 64 can be driven by 3 input AND's. This allows us to select a cell given an address, but it does not perform the important inverse function: to discover the address of a responder. To accomplish this, we perform a binary search through address space. First, we write a 1 in bit X of the desired cell and 0 in bit X of every other cell. (X might be the bit

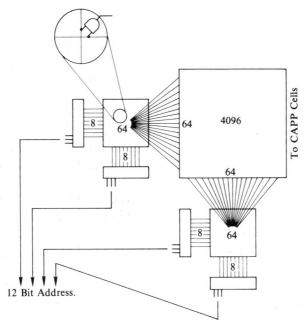

Fig. 10.9 Dual access switching tree.

used for carry or some other bit). Now we execute the following algorithm for each bit of the address:

1. Load R from W_x
2. Set R with THIS of cell with Trial Address.
3. Select first.
4. Output W_x
5. If Output = 1, Trial Address is too large (or just right).
   If Output = 0, Trial Address is too small.

The first two steps result in two cells having their R bits set to *one:* the unknown cell (having $W_x = 1$) and the cell whose address corresponds to the Trial address (having THIS = 1). We then select the first of these. If it is the unknown when we output W_x, we get a *one.* Otherwise we get a *zero.* If the unknown is earlier than the Trial Address, we proceed as in a binary search to a smaller new Trial Address. If we overlap successive steps 5 and 1 we will have 48 steps to resolve 12 bits, or about 5 μsec to discover the address of a responder.

CENTRAL CONTROL UNIT

The design of a general purpose central control unit is the same for a CAPP as it is for a contemporary von Neumann machine. As such, it is covered thoroughly elsewhere. What we will discuss here are the aspects that bear specifically on the CAPP of this chapter.

We are caught in something of a dilemma. On the one hand we do not want to design a mini-staran with lots of bells and whistles. On the other hand, if this book has any influence whatsoever, we must not present too simple-minded a design, lest we damn CAPP's for ever as too slow or too inefficient.

To begin with, we will propose that the machine under discussion have three memories: the CAM outlined in the previous two sections, a coordinate-addressed read-write memory for instructions, data and constants, and a high-speed (100 nsec) ROM for holding micro-instructions.

We will pass by the general registers and the RAM (random access memory) and concentrate on how the micro-instructions stored in the ROM condition and drive the CAM.

We assume a 24 bit word for the ROM with the low-order 16 bits broadcast to each cell of the CAM. The first eight bits of the ROM

1-4	Command
5	Execute
6	WRITER
7	WRITERBAR
8	C selector
9	K bit
10	Shift comparand register left
11	Shift comparand register right
12	Loop
13	Which bit address
14	Increment bit address
15	Decrement bit address

Fig. 10.10 The bits broadcast from the central control to the CAM.

word will determine which micro instruction is to be executed. Figure 10.10 shows the 16 bits broadcast.

Bits 1 through 4 establish the command. If bit 5 is *one* the command is executed but if bit 5 is *zero*, it is not. Bits 6 and 7 energize WRITER and WRITERBAR respectively. Bit 8 determines whether bit 9 (the K bit) is broadcast on the C line or whether the most significant bit of the comparand register is used instead. Bits 10 and 11 cause the comparand register to shift left or right one bit end around when set.

Bit 12 is the "loop bit" and is used to control loops in the micro-code. If it is set then one is subtracted from the count register and if the result is *not* zero, then the contents of the JAR (jump address register) is transferred to the MPC (micro program counter) causing a jump to that address. If the count register, after decrementing, is zero or if the loop bit is not set, then the next instruction in the micro-code is taken by the normal process of incrementing the MPC between fetches. By loading the JAR and the count register before entering a loop, any micro-instruction may function as the "test and loop" control by setting its loop bit. This eliminates any time penalty for looping.

Bit 13 tells which "bit address register" (BAO and BAl) to broadcast on the bit address lines and bits 14 and 15 can cause that selected bit address register to be incremented or decremented by one to select the next rightward or leftward bit on the next reference.

Other obviously necessary micro instructions include:

load register (JAR, MPC, BAO, BAl, Count) immediate
load register (as above plus comparand) from RAM

load comparand from CAM
branch if some responders
branch if no responders
branch if *msb* of comparand is *one*
branch if *msb* of comparand is *zero*
make CAM cell α be a responder.

plus a normal complement of microorders to enable the system to perform as a standard von Neumann machine in addition to its CAPP facilities.

All of the algorithms discussed above for this CAPP can be translated in obvious fashion to these micro-orders. That will be left as an exercise for the reader. We allowed 60 nanoseconds for the SOME $\cdot$ R/NO $\cdot$ R line to settle and with our present implementation it will require 100 nanoseconds to fetch up the command to test its state. This will slow the Max and Min searches from 4.3 sec for 16 bits to 4.9 sec. Other times are as given.

No mask register is provided in this machine. The initial contents of the bit address register and the count register determine the field to be searched or operated upon. Non-contiguous fields can be handled by a series of operations when they become necessary.

CONCLUSION

We have sketched the design for a mixed CAPP-von Neumann machine. Our design has been tailored for low cost and hence speed of operation has come second. Still we have found it possible to graft high-speed searches and parallel processing onto a conventional machine. It now remains for some adventurous soul to construct this machine and start to use it. Then we will discover what a dismal failure we have designed. But perhaps the second generation will be better.

BIBLIOGRAPHY

Ahrons, R., (1963). "Superconductive Associative Memories," *RCA Review,* pp. 325–354 (Sept. 1963).

Anderson, George A., (1974). "Multiple Match Resolvers: A New Design Method," *IEEE Trans. on Computers,* **C-23**, No. 12. 1317–1320 (Dec. 1974).

Batcher, Kenneth E., (1974). "STARAN Parallel Processor System Hardware," *Nat. Comp. Conf.,* pp. 405–410 (1974).

Berg, R. O., Schmitz, H. G., and Nuspl, S. J., (1972). "PEPE–An Overview of Architecture, Operation and Implementation," *Nat. Elec. Conf.,* pp. 312–317 (1972).

Bohm, C. and Jacopini, J., (1968). "Flow Diagrams, Turing Machines, and Languages with only two Formation Rules," *CACM,* **9,** No. 5, 336–371 (May 1968).

Crane, Bently, (1968). "Path Finding with Associative Memory," *IEEE Trans. on Computers,* **C17,** no. 7, 691–693, (July 1968).

Crofut, W. A. and Sottile, M. R., (1966). "Design Techniques of a Delay-Line Content-Addressed Memory," *IEEE Trans. on Electronic Computers,* **EC-15,** No. 4, 529–534, (Aug. 1966).

Davies, Paul M., (1963). "Design for an Associative Computer," *1963 IEEE Pacific Computer Conf.,* pp. 109–117. (multiply algorithm).

Dawoud, Dawoud and El-Araby, Nadia., (1973). "Parallel Digital Differential Analyzer with Arbitrary Stored Interconnections," *IEEE Trans. on Computers* **C-22,** No. 1, 41–46, (Jan. 1973).

Digby, David W. (1973). "A Search Memory for Many-to-Many Comparisons," *IEEE Trans. on Computers,* **C-22,** No. 8, 768–772, (Aug. 1973).

Erwin, Jerry D. and Jensen, E. Douglas, (1970). "Interrupt Processing with Queued Content-Addressable Memories," *Proc. FJCC,* pp. 621–627, (1970).

Estrin, G. and Fuller, R. H., (1963A). "Some Applications for Content Address-able Memories," *FJCC*, pp. 495–508, (1963).

Estrin, G. and Fuller, R., (1963B). "Algorithms for Content-Addressable Memories," *1963 IEEE Pacific Computer Conf.*, pp. 118–130.

Ewing, Richard G. and Davies, Paul M., (1964). "An Associative Processor," *Proc. FJCC*, pp. 147–158, (1964).

Falkoff, A. D., (1962). "Algorithms for Parallel-Search Memories," *JACM* **9** No. 10, 488–511, (Oct. 1962).

Favor, J., (1964). "A Method of Obtaining the Exact Count of Responses Using Full- and Half-Adders," *AP-111770*, Goodyear Aerospace Corporation, Akron, Ohio, (Oct. 1964).

Feldman, Jerome A. and Rovner, Paul D., (1969). "An Algol-Based Associative Language," *CACM*, **12**, No. 8, 439–449, (Aug. 1969).

Feldman, James D. and Fulmer, Louis C. (1974). "RADCAP - An Operational Parallel Processing Facility," *Nat. Comp. Conf.*, pp. 7–15, (1974).

Feng, Tse-Yun, (1968). "A Magnetic Associative Memory," *Proc. SJCC*, pp. 275–281, (1968).

Findler, Nicholas, (1968). "User's Manual for the Associative Memory and Parallel Processing Language AMPPL-1," Dept. of Computer Science, SUNY, Buffalo, N.Y., (1968).

Foster, Caxton C., (1964). "Parallel I/O for an Associative Memory," *GER-11772*, Goodyear Aerospace Corporation, Akron, Ohio, (Oct. 1964).

Foster, Caxton C., (1965). Parallel Execution of Iterative Algorithms," *GER-11857*, Goodyear Aerospace Corporation, Akron, Ohio, (Jan. 25, 1965). Also available as Ph.D. Thesis, U. of Michigan, Ann Arbor, MI, (1965).

Foster, Caxton C. (1968). "Determination of Priority in Associative Memories," *IEEE Trans. on Computers*, **C-17** No. 8, 788–789, (Aug. 1968).

Foster, Caxton C., (1965). Parallel Execution of Iterative Algorithms," *GER-11857*, Goodyear Aerospace Corporation, Akron, Ohio, (Jan. 25, 1965).

Foster, Caxton C., (1970A). "Some Simple Algorithms for Content Addressable Memories," *TN-CS-00016*, Technical Note, Computer and Information Science, Dept. Univ. of Mass., Amherst, MA, (July, 1970).

Foster Caxton C., (1970B). "A Simulated Associative Memory," TNCS-00023, Computer Science Department, Univ. of Mass., Amherst, MA. (Dec. 1970).

Foster, Caxton C. and Stockton, Fred, (1971). "Counting Responders in an Associative Memory," *IEEE Trans. on Computers*, **C-20** No. 12, 1580–1584, (Dec. 1971).

Fuller, R. H., (1963). "Content Addressable Memory Systems," *Report No. 63-25*, Dept. of Engineering, UCLA, Los Angeles, CA, (June 1963).

Fuller, R. H., Tu, J. D., and Bird, R. M., (1965A). "A Woven Plated-Wire Associative Memory," *Nat. Aerospace Elec. Conf. Proc.*, pp. 1–13, (1965).

Fuller, R. H. and Bird, R. M., (1965B). "An Associative Parallel Processor with Application to Picture Processing," *FJCC*, pp. 105–116, (1965).

Fuller, R H., (1967). "Associative Parallel Processing," *Proc. SJCC*, pp. 471–475, (1967).

Gabor, D., (1969). "Associative Holographic Memories," *IBM J. Res. Develop.* pp. 156–159, (March 1969).

Gauss, E. J., (1961). "Locating the Largest Word in a File Using a Modified Memory," *JACM* 8, 418–425, (1961).

Gilmore, Paul A., (1965A). "Parallel Compilation," *GER-12210*, Goodyear Aerospace Corp., Akron, Ohio (June 1965).

Gilmore, Paul A., (1965B). "A Parallel Compiler Simulation," *GER-12261*, Goodyear Aerospace Corp., Akron, Ohio, (Aug. 1965).

Gilmore, Paul A., (1971). "Numerical Solution of Partial Differential Equations by Associative Processing," *Proc. FJCC*, pp. 411–418, (1971).

Goodyear Aerospace Corp., (1965A). "Preliminary Programming Manual for the RADC 2048 Word Memory," *AP-112286*, Goodyear Aerospace Corp., Akron, Ohio, (1965).

Goodyear Aerospace Corp., (1965B). "The Impact of Associative and Parallel Techniques in the Field of Information Processing," *GER-11946*, Goodyear Aerospace Corp., Akron, Ohio, (Jan. 1965).

Goodyear Aerospace Corp., (1965C). *Hybrid Associative Computer Study*, 1 and 2, RADC-TDR-65, Rome Air Development Center, Griffiss Air Force Base, N.Y., (Sept. 1965).

Goodyear Aerospace Corp., (1972A) "STARAN *S* APPLE–Programming Manual," *GER-15637*, Goodyear Aerospace Corp., Akron, Ohio, (June 1972).

Goodyear Aerospace Corp., (1972B). "STARAN *S*: Reference Manual," *GER-15636*, Goodyear Aerospace Corp., Akron, Ohio, (June 1972).

Goodyear Aerospace Corp., (1972C). "Associative Processors in Data Base Management Systems," *AP-122891*, Goodyear Aerospace Corp. Akron, Ohio, (August 1972).

Harding, Philip A. and Rolund, Michael W., (1968). "2 1/2 *D* Core Search Memory," *Proc. FJCC, pp.* 1213–1218, (1968).

Hill, C.A., (1965). "Fast Adding Technique to Obtain Exact Count of AM Responders," *GER-12181*, Goodyear Aerospace Corp., Akron, Ohio, (May 1965).

Johnson, L. R. and McAndrew, M.H., (1964). "On Ordered Retrieval from an Associative Memory," *IBM Journal*, pp. 189–193, (April 1964).

Kaplan, Albert, (1963). "A Search Memory Subsystem for a General Purpose Computer," *Proc. FJCC* pp. 193–200. (1963).

Kautz, William H., (1969). "Cellular Logic-in-Memory Arrays," *IEEE Trans. on Computers*, **C-18**, No. 8, 719–727, (Aug. 1969).

Koo, J. T., (1970). "Integrated Circuit Content Addressable Memories," *IEEE Trans. on Solid State Circuits*, pp. 208–215, (Oct. 1970).

Kruse, Bjorn, (1973). "A Parallel Picture Processing Machine," *IEEE Trans. on Computers*, **C-22**, No. 12, 1075–1087, (Dec. 1973).

Lamport, Leslie, (1974). "The Parallel Execution of DO Loops," *CACM*, **17**, No. 2, 83–93, (Feb. 1974).

Lee, C. Y., (1962). "Intercommunicating Cells Basis for a Distributed Logic Computer," *Proc. FJCC*, pp. 130–136, (1962).

Levitt, K. N., and Kautz, W. H., (1972). "Cellular Arrays for the Solution of Graph Problems," *CACM* **15**, No. 9, 789–801, (Sept. 1972).

Lewin, Morton H., (1962). "Retrieval of Ordered Lists from a Content-Addressed Memory," *RCA Review*, pp. 215–229, (June 1962).

Lipovski, G. J., (1969). "The Architecture of a Large Distributed Logic Associative Memory," *Report R-424*, Coordinated Science Lab., U. of Illinois, Urbana, IL, (July 1969).

McKeever, B. T., (1965). "The Associative Memory Structure," *Proc. FJCC*, pp. 371-388, (1965).

Meilander, W. C., (1968). "The Associative Processor in Aircraft Conflict Detection," *Nat. Aerospace Elect. Conf.*, pp. 57-62, (1968).

Mills, Harlan, (1972). "Mathematical Foundations for Structured Programs," *FSC 72-6012*, Federal Systems Division, IBM, Gaithersberg, MD., (1972).

Minker, Jack, (1971). "An Overview of Associative or Content-Addressable Memory Systems and a KWIC Index to the Literature 1956-1970," *Computing Reviews*, pp. 453-504, (Oct. 1971).

Natarajan, N. K., and Thomas, Paul A. V., (1969). "A Multi-access Associative Memory," *IEEE Trans on Computers*, C-18, No. 5, 424-428, (May 1969).

Parhami, Behrooz, (1973). "Associative Memories and Processors: An Overview and Selected Bibliography," *Proc. IEEE*, **61**, No. 6, 722-730, (June 1973).

Rosin, Robert F., (1962). "An Organization of an Associative Cryogenic Computer," *Proc. SJCC*, pp. 203-211, (1962).

Rudolph, J. A., (1969). "The Associative Processor, a New Computer Resource," *GER-14087*, Goodyear Aerospace Corp., Akron, Ohio, (Feb. 1969).

Rudolph, J. A., Fulmer, Louis E., and Meilander, Willard C., (1971). "The Coming of Age of the Associative Processor," *Electronics*, **44**, No. 3, 91-96, (Feb. 15, 1971).

Rux, Peter T., (1969). "A Glass Delay Line Content Addressed Memory System," IEEE Trans. on Computers, Vol. C-18, No. 6, June 1969, pp. 512-520.

Sakaguchi, M. Nishida, N., and Nemoto, T., (1970). "A New Associative Memory System Utilizing Holography," *IEEE Trans. on Computers*, C-19, No. 12, 1174-1181, (Dec. 1970).

Seeber, Robert R., Jr. (1960). "Associative Self-Sorting Memory," *Proc. Eastern JCC*, pp. 179-187, (1960).

Seeber, R. R. and Lindquist, A. B., (1962). "Associative Memory with Ordered Retrieval," *IBM Journal*, pp. 126-136, (Jan. 1962).

Shore, John E., (1973). "Second Thoughts on Parallel Processing," *Comput. and Elect. Eng.*, **1**, 95-109, Pergamon Press, (1973).

Slade, A. E. and McMahon, (1956). "A Cryotron Catalog Memory System," *Proc. Eastern JCC*, pp. 115-119, (1956).

Slotnick, Daniel L., (1967). "Unconventional Systems," *Proc. SJCC*, pp. 477-481, (1967).

Stillman, Neil J. and Defiore, Casper R., (1971). "Associative Processing of Line Drawings," *Proc. SJCC*, pp. 557-562, (1971).

Stone, Harold S., (1971). "Associative Processing for General Purpose Computers Through Use of Modified Memories," *Proc. FJCC*, pp. 951-955, (1968).

Swartzlander, Earl E., Jr. (1973). "Parallel Counters," *IEEE Trans. on Computers*, C-22, No. 11, pp. 1021-1024, (Nov. 1973).

Thurber, Kenneth J. and Patton, Peter C., (1973). "The Future of Parallel Processing," *IEEE Trans. on Computers*, C-22, No. 12, pp. 1140-1143, (Dec. 1973).

Unger, S. H., (1958). "A Computer Oriented Toward Spatial Problems," *Proc. IRE*, pp. 1744–1750 (Oct. 1958).

Urban, Roger A., (1972). "An Airborne Associative Array Processor," *Nat. Elect. Conf.*, pp. 318–321, (1972).

Wald, L. D., Armstrong, T. R., Huang, C. C., and Saxton, T. L., (1973). "Evaluation of the Use of an Associative Processor in Communication Multiplexing," *RADC-TR-73-19*, Final Technical Report, Rome Air Development Center, Griffiss Air Force Base, N. Y. (Feb. 1973).

Weinstein, H., (1963). "Proposals for Ordered Sequential Detection of Simultaneous Multiple Responses," *IEEE Trans. on Elect. Comp.*, **EC-12**, No. 10, pp. 564–567, (Oct. 1963).

Wesley, M. A., (1969). "Associative Parallel Processing for the Fast Fourier Transform," *IEEE Trans. on Audio and Electro Acoustics*, **AU-17**, No. 2 pp. 162–165, (June 1969).

Wolinsky, A., (1968). "A Simple Proof of Lewin's Ordered-Retrieval Theorem for Associative Memories," *CACM*, **11**, No. 7, 448–490, (July 1968).

Wolinsky, Albert, (1969). "Unified Interval Classification and Unified 3-Classification for Associative Memories," *IEEE Trans. on Computers*, **C-18**, No. 10, pp. 899–911, (Oct. 1969).

INDEX

INDEX